Food for Lovers

Food for Lovers

Menus for lovers
affluent or impecunious,
in a hurry
or with time to spare

Composed by Pamela Michael
from recipes by
KATIE STEWART, KENNETH LO
and others

**PADDINGTON
PRESS LTD**

NEW YORK & LONDON

Library of Congress Cataloging in Publication Data

Stewart, Katie.
    Food for lovers.

    Includes index.
    1. Cookery. 2. Menus. I. Lo, Kenneth H. C.,
joint author. II. Michael, Pamela. III. Title.
TX652.S718   641.5   77-4373
ISBN 0-448-22678-2

IN THE UNITED STATES
PADDINGTON PRESS LTD.
Distributed by
GROSSET & DUNLAP

IN THE UNITED KINGDOM
PADDINGTON PRESS LTD.

IN CANADA
Distributed by
RANDOM HOUSE OF CANADA LTD.

IN AUSTRALIA
Distributed by
ANGUS & ROBERTSON PTY. LTD.

IN SOUTHERN AFRICA
Distributed by
ERNEST STANTON (PUBLISHERS) (PTY.) LTD.

Contents

It's all a question of aim

There's nothing in the world like love,
So delicate and floury.
The sweetest flower has not its power;
It is so soft and savoury.
I wonder why cooks do not try
To use it as a spice;
A tiny trickle our tongues would tickle,
It is so very nice.

Plautus: Casina

Introduction

I remember, many years ago, reading a French novel in which the inevitable bedroom scene was made memorable by the girl saying to her lover when the act of love was scarcely over: "What do you like for breakfast?" The man was so shocked that she could think of anything as mundane as food at such a moment, that it precipitated for him the end of the affair.

But how wrong he was! She was only wanting to gratify her beloved's every desire and, if she didn't happen to have his particular cereal in the larder, she would happily have dived for her coat and gone to get it. Perhaps you could say that in those "pre-Liberation" days she was the perfect lover, because, in her, sweetness and consideration were combined with realism and the knowledge that food is as important to the lover as to anyone. She knew that in a few hours' time he would be demanding to be fed – and she wanted to spoil and pander.

That most famous of early cookery writers, El Baghdadi, arranged man's pleasures into six categories: food, drink, clothes, sex, scent and sound, and himself rated the pleasure of eating highest, for, as he rightly said, "no other pleasure can be enjoyed unless a man has good health, to which food is ancillary."

The importance of food to lovers was recently reaffirmed by Professor James McCary, who says that there is a closer connection between eating and sexual desire than most

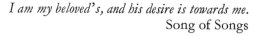

I am my beloved's, and his desire is towards me.
Song of Songs

Music may be a food of love, but how much do you provide?
And when do you stop making music and start making love?

Certainly, too much music can be counter-productive!

people realize: "a well-fed body naturally includes 'well-nourished' sexual organs capable of vigorous and continuous expression." In classical times you find Ovid, as he describes in his *Metamorphoses*, when the mood has come upon him after a good dinner, sending a slave to his mistress to acquaint her of the excited state of his loins and to ask if she could receive him at once! McCary, too, says: "When one has eaten a carefully prepared, subtly seasoned meal, together with wine, in an ambience enhanced by soft music and glowing candles, one experiences a delightful glow – not only of the senses, but also of the body." . . . Most of us will have experienced this, as also how, as Dr. Balzli writes:

The Devil, here seen in the guise of a girl intent on seducing a bishop, obviously considered food and drink necessary accessories for such an enterprise. No doubt they would have proved effective, but for the untimely interference of St. Andreas (haloed, right).

If Madame Potiphar had had a copy of this book, this embarrassing situation might never have arisen.

"After a perfect meal we are more susceptible to the ecstasy of love than at any other time." Or, in the words of Hercules de Saxonia: "such are aprest to love that are young and lusty, live at ease, stall-fed, free from cares, like cattle in a rank pasture, idle and solitary persons, they must needs *hirquitallire*." For this reason, Savonarola directed a charge of lechery against "Monks, Friars and religious persons, because they live solitary, fair daintily, and do nothing." And a 16th-century author, L. de Avila, counseled all who are thin or skinny to avoid "unchastity" as they would their enemy.

To eat small birds and doves was long considered an aid to husbands and lovers in the performance of their marital duties

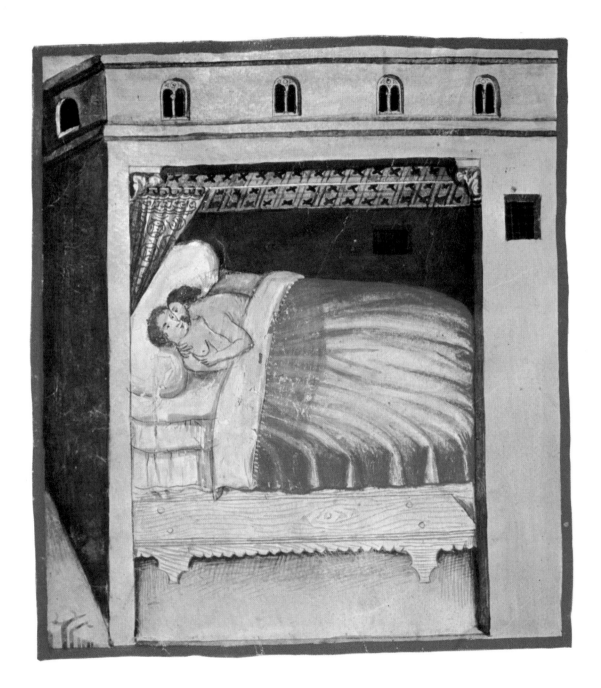

and the prudent housewife catered accordingly.

Obviously, if one is to eat well, someone has to cook well. Here there seems to be some difference of opinion between East and West, for while the West lays emphasis on excellence in the food provided for lovers, the author of the famous *Kama Sutra*, listing the sixty-four arts that the female who wishes to succeed should study, puts the culinary art at No. 23, way behind such seemingly inessential skills as "fixing stained glass into a floor," which even precedes the art of "making beds and spreading out carpets and cushions for reclining." It would seem that the way to an Indian's heart was less through the stomach than it is to the heart of a Westerner. This may be partly because traditionally men and women do not eat the main meals together. What they share are rather the refreshments, the cakes and sweetmeats that the *Kama Sutra* recommends should accompany dalliance.

*In India the way to a man's heart
is less through his stomach*

than is reputedly the case in the West.

Certainly, in Europe, food and sex have always been closely associated. The famous Democritus Junior writes that it is "a rare thing to see a young man or a woman that lives idly, and fares well, of what condition soever, not to be in love. Alcibiades was still dallying with wanton young women, immoderate in his expenses, effeminate in his apparel, ever in love, but why? He was over-delicate in his diet, too frequent and excessive in banquets. . . . Lust and security domineer together. . . . " – all of which the wife of Bath in Chaucer freely justifies,

> For all so soker as cold engendrith hayl,
> A likorous mouth must have a licorous tail.

Of course, there are the extreme cases of those in the first euphoria of calf-love or in the depths of lover's despair, who may not notice or care what is on the plate in front of them, if they are able to eat at all, but to lovers in general food is important. For the man, it might bolster him up when virility is flagging owing to age or over-indulgence: "A man obtains sexual vigor," says the *Kama Sutra*, "by drinking milk mixed with sugar, the root of the uchchata, the piber chaba, and liquorice."

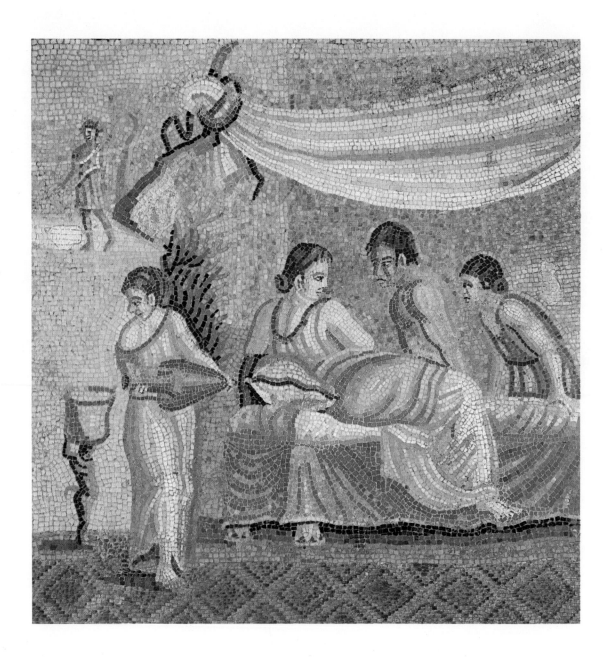

Alcohol removes inhibitions and weakens the will to say 'no',

but it is white wine that contains the most phosphorus, which is the aphrodisiac, so make sure that you have an adequate supply.

The combat between Love and Chastity.

Not only that, but "if a man mixes rice with the eggs of the sparrow, and having boiled this in milk, adds to it ghee and honey, and drinks as much of it as necessary, he will be able to enjoy innumerable women."

But, perhaps more importantly, in the West at least, the food a lover provides is an indication of the care, trouble and expense to which one is prepared to go and that, one hopes, will be evidence of the depths of one's feelings. Love in a garret with a meal of fish and chips, or its equivalent, eaten off a paper plate, can be romantic, but there is as much, if not more to be said for candlelight and silver as an accompaniment to choice food, as McCary agrees. Apart from this aspect of it, in antiquity and the Middle Ages especially, people thought that many foods had qualities that would either lend vigor to one's own love-making or would stimulate desire in the object of one's attentions and so, perhaps, turn "no" into "yes."

In olden times, after the world had lost the Ancient Egyptian art of contraception by acupuncture of the ear lobe, love-making involved an initial combat between love and chastity, an amatory jousting that the Pill has now rendered unnecessary. This was why for so many centuries people had recourse to aphrodisiacs, potions and philters; the women to help them get their men, the men to help them overcome ladies' resistance.

The most famous of all reputed aphrodisiacs is rhinoceros horn and next comes the Korean plant, ginseng. There seems to be nothing to support the claims of rhinoceros horn, though apparently ginseng can be efficacious to some degree. Ginseng is a native of Korea, where it grows in the glens and on the slopes of the Kang-ge mountains. It used to be considered a panacea for all ills and was sold wrapped in goldfish skin and white silk. The recipient was enjoined to cover his nose and mouth before he unpacked it. It was cooked in a special silver kettle with a lining, like a double saucepan, and the infusion that resulted was drunk either on its own or with rice wine. Ginseng is what the emperors of China used to send to high officials as a present when they retired – and how much nicer than a gold watch or a knighthood. Also easier to acquire, as you can now buy ginseng tea, etc., in the Chinese supermarkets. On the whole, however, there is little evidence that ginseng or anything else one eats or drinks will work this particular miracle, but when the food or drink recommended is itself pleasant, why not give it the benefit of the doubt?

Ideas of which foods were aphrodisiac have differed widely, and it almost looks as though people have attributed their successes in courtship or seduction to what they had eaten (or given the other to eat) on that particular occasion. Sometimes these views contradict each other: for example, you find the Egyptians holding the lettuce sacred to their ithyphallic deity Min, while the Greeks and the Flopsy Bunnies considered it to be soporific. Some people considered rice an anti-aphrodisiac, yet the rice-eating peoples are as famous lovers as any. The cucumber, according to Andrew Boorde, "creates shuddering feelings and engenders bile, and is a great preventive against amatory feelings." It almost seems that one man's aphrodisiac is another man's soporific.

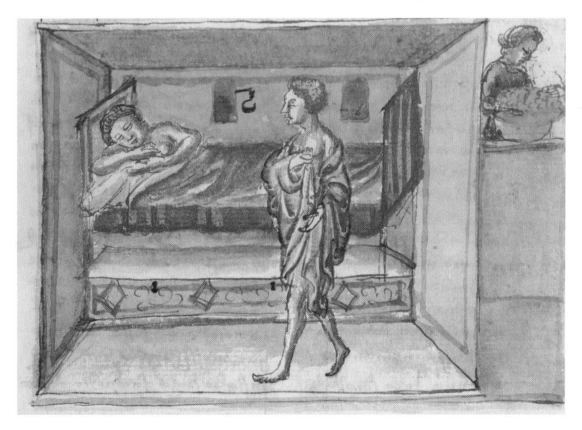

The Age of Reason ushered in a tendency to pooh-pooh the whole idea of the aphrodisiac, holding that the only effective agent was the man or woman's own physical attraction and charm, and by and large that view is held today. But there are drugs with aphrodisiac properties, though they are neither easy to come by nor easy to use. One such is obtained from the roots of the mandrake, which Rachel is supposed to have eaten before she attracted the notice of Jacob, hence the conception and birth of Joseph. Circe is reputed to have used it in her love potions, and in Persia it was much used to secure a husband's love, though they found that if eaten with pickles, it would drive the eater off his head. There was a great deal of hocus-pocus about obtaining mandrake: amongst other things, it was best plucked by tying a cord round the plant, fastening this to the collar of a dog, who was then called away, thus pulling the shrieking roots out of the ground as he ran off to join his master. However, many people firmly believed in its magic.

Other of the more exotic supposed aphrodisiacs are obtained from the thorn-apple and certain plants that only grow in Africa or South America. As well as being difficult to obtain, these drugs are dangerous to use, not only because there is no guarantee that the desire aroused will be directed at the person administering the drug, but chiefly because the margin between the sexually effective and the lethal dose is so small that it would require more experiment than the law would allow for anyone to acquire enough experience to handle them effectively. The same applies to the insect called the Spanish Fly (cantharides) which, dried, was in its day a very popular aphrodisiac, as was the somewhat similar Telini Fly that lovers used from Italy to China. Both insects contain considerable amounts of cantharides which, in certain quantities, will induce priapism; the danger lies in the fact that only a slight increase in the dose will result in most painful death. Cantharides was used in the notorious and near fatal case of Elizabeth Ewiot of Balhousie (1601), when her father's cook tried to gain her favors by underhanded means, having failed with his own natural charm. The cook had sought the help of a bookbinder in Perth who promised "he vald gif the sum Spanye fleis, callit cantarides, quhilk, gif thow suld move the said Elizabeth to drink of, it vald mak hir out of all questione, to grene efter the."

It was easy for the cook to administer the potion, which induced such violent vomiting it nearly cost the poor girl her life. The cook had the good sense to give her milk to drink, an antidote well known since antiquity (goat's milk is reputedly the best), and the girl recovered. The cook tried again with a similar result. He then used force, while the girl's parents were absent, made her pregnant and then tried to make her drink an abortion potion. It was this that finally brought him before the court.

Reading the old books you see how little there is to which people have not at some time attributed aphrodisiac properties. This is, probably, because any success (or failure) in courtship or seduction was attributed to the menu chosen for that particular occasion.

Robert Burton gives a list of what he calls "lascivious meats" that starts with wine in

The mandrake to which Rachel and so many others are reputed to have had recourse.

Sweet is snow in summer for one athirst to drink, and sweet for sailors after winter to see the crown of spring;
but most sweet when one cloak hides two lovers, and the praise of love is told by both.

Asclepiades

generous quantities, peas, broad beans, radishes (especially when well seasoned and peppered), artichokes, lettuce, colewort, leeks, onions, pine-nuts, sweet almonds, snails, mussels, mead, fruit, etc. He concludes with the motto: *Post prandia Callyroenda*.

In the old days, when there was very little waste, since people ate pretty well every part of the animals they butchered – ears, palates, udders, eyes, etc. – certain things like the testicles of bulls and rams, suggested themselves as aphrodisiacs. Here, of course, they were on the right track, because testicles contain testosterone. What people in those days did not know, and could not have known, was that, even if it survives the process of being cooked, the digestive juices of the stomach swiftly render the active factor in testosterone ineffective. The only effective way to administer it is subcutaneously.

The ancients were also on the right track in recommending fish and shellfish to those in search of "venery," since modern chemistry has discovered that they contain enough phosphorus and glycero-phosphates to have an effect, though we have not yet been told how much fish you have to eat to obtain results.

Whether or not this virtue is to be found in other foods recommended (say, doves, asparagus, ginger, truffles, etc.) has yet to be established, but it would seem that one's own physical charms and magnetism are the best and the most reliable aphrodisiac that one can employ. Grapes, pomegranates (the sweet variety), "excite Venus"; asparagus, artichokes, tarragon and garlic all "provoke urine and Venus." Where garlic is concerned one may quote *Dyets dry dinner*:

"Garlicke, onion and Leekes are very holesome; but the savour is passing loathsome and offensive. Wherefore some have thought of a medicament to take away the sent of them. But none like Syr Thomas More. To take away the smell of onions, eat Leekes and to convince your Leekes, eate a clove or two of garlicke; and if the garlicke be strong, choke him with a piece of T. with a *u*. with an *r* with a *d*."

Right up to the Age of Reason people were firmly convinced of the aphrodisiac properties of certain foods and specifics, but where the affections of the loved one were concerned, your love being unrequited, many felt that more direct methods were required and this is when people in that predicament had recourse to love philters. As often as not these were administered with the best intentions and, shall we say? the highest motives, and so can be classed as white magic as opposed to the black arts of the seducer's brews. It was mostly women who resorted to them, but not exclusively: Othello was accused of using a philter on Desdemona. In the *Arabian Nights* there is a description of the love potion prepared for the love-lorn merchant, Sham-al-Din. The apothecary having accepted the commission, "betook himself to a hashish seller, of whom he bought two ounces of concentrated Roumi opium and equal parts of Chinese cubebs, cinnamon, cloves, cardamons, ginger, white pepper, and mountain shiek;* and pounding them all together boiled them in sweet olive oil; after which he added three ounces of male frankincense in fragments and a cupful of coriander seed, and macerating the whole made

*A lizard reputed to be aphrodisiac if merely held in the hand.

it into an electuary with Roumi bee honey. Then he put the confection in the bowl and carried it to the merchant, saying: 'Take of my electuary with a spoon after supping, and wash it down with a sherbert made of rose conserve; but first sup off mutton and house pigeon plentifully seasoned and hotly spiced.'"

It would appear that at certain times girls have had a hard time of it. "In vain might the tender mother anxiously caution her beloved offspring to beware of her most dangerous enemy – man. Of what avail was the warning against the stratagems converting every ingredient of sorcery to fan the latest flame or lull suspected guile?

"Hence were animal, vegetable and mineral products employed, – the use of stimulating food and deleterious potions: both productive of temporary distress or permanent injury, when administered to those on whom the treacherous plot was perpetrated." (J. G. Dalyell: *The Darker Superstitions of Scotland*, 1834). In other words: if you must be good, be careful.

A famous man said to have been unfairly captivated by the use of love philters was Philip of Macedon, father of Alexander the Great. However, when the queen, Olympias, saw the girl in question and how pretty and attractive she was, she admitted that such a girl had no need of philters.

Lucretia used to brag that her body could do more than all "Philosophers, Astrologers, Necromancers, Witches, and the rest of the crew. As for potions and philters I could never skill of them, the sole Philter that I ever used was kissing and embracing, by which alone I made men rave like beasts stupefied, and compelled them to worship me like an idol."

In the 15th century Lady Grey was accused of gaining the affections of Edward IV by means of a love philter. Two centuries later Madame Montespan paid the huge sum of fifty crowns for one, and people are using them still.

One of the common ingredients of philters was myrtle, which was supposed to have been used by Venus in her "most intimate toilet." The following is an old recipe for "mirtle water" which "mixed with cordial syrups is a good cordial and inclines those that drink it to be very amorous":

"The flowers and leaves of mirtle, two handfuls, infuse them in two quarts of spring water, and a quart of white wine, twenty-four hours, and then distil them in a cold still and this will be of strong scent and tincture, and by adding more or less mirtle you may make it stronger or weaker as you please."

This myrtle water was used in the preparation of angel water, a Portuguese invention: this called for a pint of orange-flower water, a pint of rose water and half a pint of myrtle water. To this you added two-thirds of a pint of distilled spirit of musk and the same amount of ambergris.

Ambergris in the East is still thought to be a potent aphrodisiac and coffee is often served in cups in the bottom of which is a small hollow into which a piece of ambergris is supposed to be placed.

Where intentions are honest and the food really good

the way to a man's heart may well be through the stomach.

The obvious way of administering your philter is at the dining table in either the food or the drink. But what food and what drink?

Turkey-cocke or Ginny-cocke were reputed to "enflame Venus"; pigeons and eggs "excite Venus," while ginger "provoketh sluggish husbands." Chestnuts "being flatulent incite Venus and wrought with honey and sugars, cure the biting of mad dogs" (and Englishmen?). Pistake (sic) nuts "purge the brest: strengthen the reynes and stomacke; open obstructions of the liver and stay dispositions to vomit: heale the biting of serpents: provoke Venus wondrously."

The number of foods recommended as being helpful in "venery" range from sparrows' brains and beetles, mussels, eggs, calves' feet and crocodile meat stewed in white wine to such humdrum things as the onion. Neither of the first two will be available on the shelves of your supermarket, and, unless you live on the banks of the Limpopo, there is little chance of your being able to include crocodile in your menu. Mussels, eggs, even calves' feet present no difficulties, still less onions which the Greeks said "dim the eyes, and excite the amatory propensities," especially the kind known as "royal onions." But the Greeks were cute enough to warn people that "the onion will do you no good if you have no strength yourself."

As we have seen an infinite variety of foods have at one time or another been thought to be of assistance in venery. It would be intriguing if one could know what dishes Hero served to Leander when he came in dripping from his hour-long swim across the Hellespont; or what Helen ate before they had to introduce rationing in Troy. What fare did Solomon's cooks provide for the Queen of Sheba? Unfortunately, we do not know, any more than we know what was grown in the kitchen gardens of Cythera and Lesbos. It has been suggested that the liaison between Tristan and Isolde was triggered off by the fish they were constrained to eat on the voyage from Ireland.

All that is shrouded in mystery; but there can be no doubt that food is important, despite the dissident opinion of Avila (16th century) who warns his reader not to indulge in "matrimonial labor" when hungry or sated with food and drink. One is entitled to assume that Madame Butterfly's menus palled on Lieutenant Pinkerton and that a more imaginative diet might have saved the situation. I think one can say that the delights of Leah's table, as well as of her other articles of furniture, played a part in keeping Chèri ensnared so long, but it is no use pretending that food is the only thing.

The act of cooking can itself be attractive, as it was to the "I" of *The Golden Ass* when he found Fotis mincing meat and making potage. It is not quite clear what Fotis was wearing, but "she was girded about her body under the paps with a swathell of red silk." She stirred the pot and turned the meat with an action that was reciprocated lower down, so that "her loynes and hips did likewise move and shake, which was in my mind a comely sight to see."

But, suppose she had been wearing nothing but her red silk swathell, would that have made her more attractive? When John Lerius got to Brazil, he and his companions found the inhabitants naked as they were born, "without any covering, so much of their privities," nor could the French persuade them to wear any. Why, one wonders, did they even try? Was it because the native women were not all that shapely to Western eyes? Certainly the French, who were there for a good year, found the native women's nakedness neither provocative nor an "incitement to lust." In fact after a year of "commerce with naked women" they decided that women with clothes on were much more attractive. Is this, perhaps, a question of age? David was enflamed by the sight of Bathsheba, the Elders by their glimpses of Susannah. Sestius Gallus was already "an old lecher" when he had naked girls wait upon him and his guests at table. The Babylonians are supposed to have had "lascivious queans dance frisking in that fashion" at their entertainments; and at Tuscan banquets the guests were served by naked women. Obviously, there is more to attraction and seduction than the body that meets the eye.

For one thing there is drink. People very early discovered how alcohol breaks down the inhibitions and weakens the will to say "no." The chemist tells us that white wine contains phosphorus which is an aphrodisiac, hence the tradition that champagne is the seducer's best weapon. On the other hand, in Scandinavia a swain will treat his girl to a bottle of port and achieve the same effect, and who in China could dispute the claims of rice wine?

One bed shall serve for us when asleep . . . we will always drink from the same cup.
Propertius

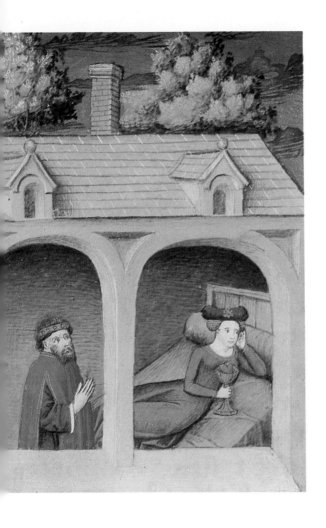

*The combination of bedroom and sitting room
is as old as time and, for the lover, perhaps
the most useful invention Like smoking,
you can indulge in love between courses and
before or after the meal, just as the flesh
moves you.*

Long ago Rufinus wrote:

"I am armed against love with a breastplate of Reason, neither shall he conquer me, one against one; yes, I a mortal will contend with the immortal: but if he have Bacchus to second him, what can I do alone against the two?"

The author of the *Kama Sutra* lays down the procedure to be followed:

"In the pleasure room, decorated with flowers, and fragrant with perfumes, attended by his friends and servants, the man will receive the woman, who will come bathed and dressed, and will invite her to take refreshment and to drink freely. He should then seat her on his left side, and holding her hair, and touching also the end and knot of her garment, he should gently embrace her with his right arm. They should then carry on an amusing conversation on various subjects, and may also talk suggestively of things which would be considered as coarse, or not to be mentioned generally in society. They may then sing, either with or without gesticulations, and play on musical instruments, talk about the arts, and persuade each other to drink. At last when the woman is overcome with love and desire, he shall dismiss the people that may be with him . . . and then when the two are left alone, they should proceed as has already been described in the previous chapters."

But the lover must remember that there must be moderation in all things, alcohol especially, because in excess it can easily become counterproductive.

Avec nous amans et buveurs,
Venez partager les douceurs
Que nous goutons sous cette treille
C'est dans le jus de la bouteille
Que Cupidon trompe ses traits
Si quelque fois sous cet ombrage frais
Ce Dieu s'en dort, Bacchus l'eveille.

The idea that love-making was such an intimate act that it should be performed only in the privacy of one's room (at home, in a *chambre separée* or an hotel), seems an invention of the 19th and 20th centuries; certainly in antiquity and the Middle Ages it was accepted that flirting, courtship and actual physical love-making were just as much group activities that could be performed in the company of the like-minded, hence the Jardins d'Amour, the Liebesgärten, to which the young forgathered for these purposes, which are depicted in so many paintings. The Courts of Love of the troubadours were probably similar institutions. One wonders where we have got our modern bashfulness and modesty; and yet bashfulness is not a modern trait, for *The Secrets of Art & Nature* quotes Cardanus as writing: "Some that blush or fear, are hindered from Venery, and suppose they are bewitched; many things are thought to cure this disease: flying ants mixed with oyle of elders and the Man's Yard anointed therewith, and many other things." (It is interesting that in those days bashfulness was regarded as a disease.)

Equally public were the baths. Bathing has always been associated with food and love-making. Like the Edwardians no self-respecting Roman would have dined without first bathing and changing, but even in their technically highly developed civilizations few

The pleasures of dining in one's bath are recognized by all who have tried it.

people had the resources to maintain a bath of their own. Baths were public institutions – and the setting of many scandalous tales. In the Middle Ages and later this was still true, and, bathing being a lengthy, protracted business, any good bath house also provided food and beds for those requiring these facilities. Only the immensely wealthy had their own baths, though the rich would have a temporary one installed in the courtyard or grounds of their houses on special occasions, as Denis Hesselin did when entertaining

Perhaps the right food

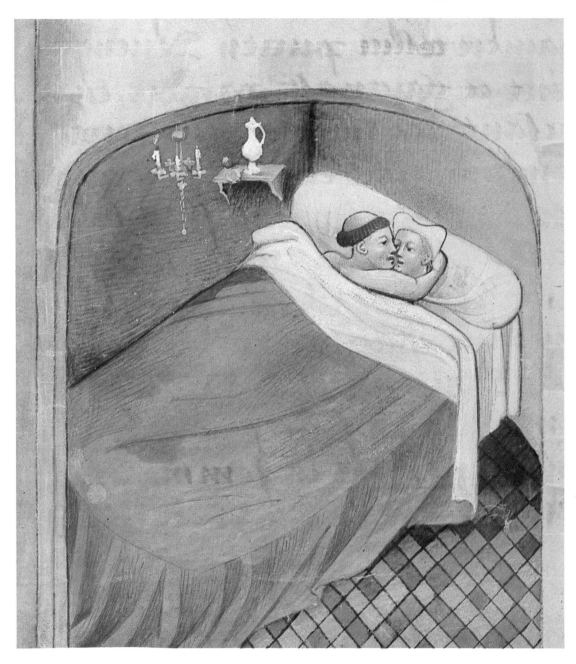

will have the right result.

Louis XI and his queen in 15th-century France. The king bathed before dining, but the queen excused herself on the grounds that she had a cold. The lesson would seem to be that the serious lover should offer the hospitality of his/her bathroom, assuming that you are dining in the intimate atmosphere of your home.

The Indian lover is recommended to have his pleasure room fragrant with perfume, and, of course, scents have always been held to have an aphrodisiac effect. Like all such claims this is impossible to prove or disprove; but moderation in the use of scents is obviously called for when you are providing a well-cooked meal of which fragrance is an integral part.

The picnic has been a favorite with lovers since the beginning of time, the food ranging from the simplest to the very elaborate. The *Kama Sutra*, listing the types of men who generally obtain success with women, puts men "who like picnics and pleasure parties" nineteenth, which is about half way down the list.

A Note on the Menus and Recipes
The menus in the following pages are arranged by the month and grouped according to the seasons. Within each month are four menus: one for the affluent and one for the impecunious lover-cook; another for the lover in a hurry and one for the lover with time to spare. To compensate for the *Kama Sutra*'s lack of enthusiasm for picnics, August contains suggestions for lover-oriented picnic fare. For lovers who are lovers of Chinese cuisine, September and October will prove particularly tempting at any time of year; November, too, contains some special suggestions for *amateurs* of Indian food. Here and there, a particularly apt wine or table decoration has been suggested. It should also be mentioned that all the dishes are ones that will not spoil if kept waiting, and many of them can be eaten with one hand!

P. M.

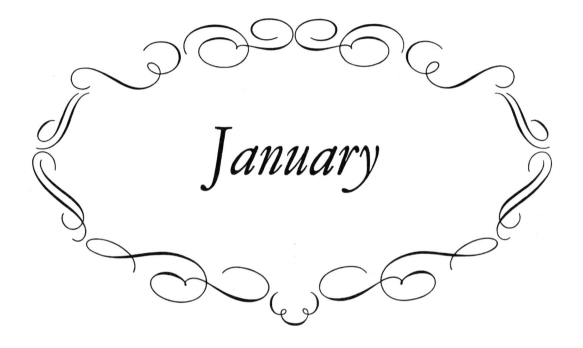

January

THE AFFLUENT LOVER

Chestnut Soup
Pork Fillets in Paprika Sauce
Mousseline Potatoes
Spinach or Tiny Sprouts
Tangerine Mousse

Use fresh chestnuts for the soup and buy the best; the larger ones are easier to peel. It can be made well in advance and reheated at the last moment when you add the cream. The pork fillets are luxuriously cooked with sherry and mushrooms and can be kept warm for a reasonable time without any harm. Serve them with mousseline potatoes (see recipe for keeping them without spoiling) and spinach, which you can cook and drain, then re-heat, turning in plenty of butter first before serving. Alternatively, if you can get some really tiny sprouts, 5 or 6 minutes in a pan of already boiling water is enough to cook them to tender crispness. After two fairly rich dishes, a tangerine mousse is a light, re-freshing ending to the meal. A good bottle of claret, St. Emilion for instance, would con-firm the idea that nothing is too good for your beloved, as would a glass of orange Curaçao with your coffee. Be extravagant in your choice of flowers. Only buy a few, and cut them short – stalks are not beautiful, and set them in a low container. Fragrant spring flowers, out-of-season and expensive, are more romantic than the stiff, ubiquitous chrysanthemum.

Chestnut Soup

Cut a slit on the flat side of each chestnut and place them in a saucepan of boiling water, reboil and simmer for 10 minutes. Drain and peel away both the outer and inner skins.

$\frac{1}{2}$ lb chestnuts
$\frac{1}{2}$ oz butter
1 small onion
$\frac{1}{2}$ pint chicken stock
freshly milled pepper

   Melt the butter in a large saucepan, Peel and finely chop the onion. Add to the pan, cover and sauté gently for about 5 minutes until tender but not brown. Add the chestnuts and the stock and bring up to the boil. Cover with a lid and simmer gently for 45 minutes to an hour, or until the chestnuts are quite tender.

   Draw the pan off the heat and pass the chestnuts and stock through a sieve, or purée the ingredients half at a time in an electric blender. Return the soup to the pan, season with salt and plenty of freshly milled pepper and reheat until hot but not boiling.

Pork Fillets in Paprika Sauce

Trim and cut the fillets into thick strips, and finely chop the onion or shallot. Heat butter in a pan and quickly fry the meat to brown on each side. Lower the heat and add the onion and paprika and cook slowly for a few minutes. Shake in the flour and stir to blend, then add the sherry and enough stock to barely cover the meat, stir constantly and bring to the boil; then cover and simmer gently for 30 minutes.

Wipe the mushrooms and sauté them in a little butter for 2 or 3 minutes, then add them to the pan of pork when it has finished cooking; keep warm, and when ready to serve, stir in the cream.

2 thick slices pork fillet
½ small onion or 1 shallot
½ oz butter
1 rounded teaspoon paprika
1 rounded teaspoon flour
2 tablespoons sherry
stock – see recipe
2 oz button mushrooms
butter to fry
2 tablespoons heavy (double) cream

Mousseline Potatoes

Peel the potatoes and boil in a pan of salted water until tender – about 20 minutes. Drain and dry thoroughly, then mash well with a fork. Beat in the butter with a wooden spoon. Boil up the milk and beat enough into the potatoes to make them light and creamy. Spread the top level with the back of the spoon and cover with 1 or 2 tablespoons taken from the hot milk. Cover the pan and leave at the back of the stove until wanted. To serve, return the pan to a moderate heat and beat up the purée before dishing.

¾ lb potatoes
water – see recipe
½ teaspoon salt
½ oz butter
milk, about ¼ pint

Spinach

Wash spinach and cook in a dry pan for 10–15 minutes, turning once or twice to cook evenly. Tip the spinach into a colander and press out as much liquid as possible. Leave to drain as long as you wish. The spinach may be prepared in advance, say the night before, and refrigerated until you are ready to reheat it and serve. To do so, melt the butter in a pan and tip in the spinach. Turn it over and over with a wooden spoon until all the butter is absorbed and the spinach heated through. Add a grating of nutmeg and serve.

1 lb spinach
2–3 oz butter
nutmeg

Tangerine Mousse

Separate the eggs and put the yolks, with the sugar and grated rind and juice of the tangerines, into a basin. Sprinkle the gelatine over the cold water in a small pan and set aside. Stand the basin with the eggs and sugar mixture over a pan of hot water and whisk for 4–5 minutes; take the basin off the heat, stand on a folded cloth, and whisk again for 4–5 minutes until the mixture is pale and thick. Stand the pan of gelatine over a low heat

2 eggs
3 oz sugar
4 tangerines
2 level teaspoons gelatine
2 tablespoons water
5 fl oz heavy (double) cream

until it dissolves and becomes quite clear. Cool for a minute and then trickle slowly into the egg mixture, hold the pan high and whisk at the same time. Whip the cream lightly and fold it into the mixture; then whisk the egg whites stiffly and fold them in with a metal spoon or a spatula. Leave in a cool place until the mousse begins to set, then stir and pour it into a pretty glass or china dish.

Chill and serve with a little light (single) cream.

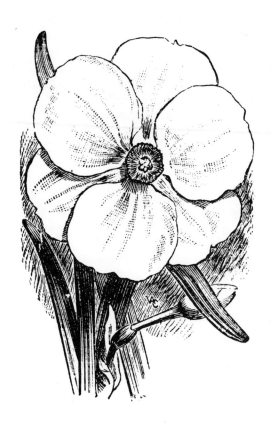

THE IMPECUNIOUS LOVER

Chicken Liver Pâté
Navarin of Lamb
White Turnips and Carrots Cooked in Butter
Pan Potatoes
Prune Mousse

This menu gives the impression that you are an excellent cook and generous provider without knocking a hole in your pocket. The navarin of lamb uses one of the less expensive cuts and is cooked with turnips and carrots that are plentiful and cheap just now; buy a few extra and they will provide a vegetable dish when diced and sweated in butter. If you whip up a small carton of cream it will be enough for the prune mousse, plus some to go with your coffee. Have a bottle of red wine and use brown earthenware dishes and a checked gingham cloth to create an informal bistro atmosphere. A red candle stuck in a bottle will cast an intimate glow.

Chicken Liver Pâté

Trim the chicken livers and sauté gently in $\frac{1}{2}$ oz butter for 3–4 minutes. Remove from the heat and put the liver and pan juices through a fine grinder (mincer) or blend in an electric blender until smooth. Stir in the sherry.

    Beat the remaining $\frac{1}{2}$ oz butter in a small bowl until soft, add the liver mixture, season with salt and pepper and beat thoroughly. Spoon the pâté into a small pot, cover with foil and chill. Serve with hot toast and butter.

3 oz chicken livers
1 oz butter
2 teaspoons sherry
salt
freshly milled black pepper
toast and butter

Navarin of Lamb

Trim any fat or gristle from the lamb and cut into neat pieces on the bone. Peel and cut the onion into quarters, peel the turnip, scrape the carrot, and cut them longways into thick strips. Heat the dripping in a pan and first fry the lamb pieces until brown on all sides, lift out, then lower the heat and tip in the vegetables and cook gently until beginning to color. Keep stirring to prevent them sticking to the pan. Stir in the flour and cook for a minute, then add the stock or water slowly and stir until smooth and thickened. Replace the meat and season with salt, pepper and a pinch of sugar. Add the herbs, cover

1 lb middle neck of lamb
1 onion
1 carrot
1 small white turnip
1 tablespoon dripping
1 level tablespoon flour
$\frac{1}{2}$ pint stock or water
$\frac{1}{2}$ level teaspoon salt
pinch of pepper
sugar – see recipe

and cook gently for 30 minutes. Remove the lid and simmer for a further 30 minutes, turning the meat over to keep it moist during the cooking time. To thicken and reduce the gravy turn up the heat a little before serving, but until this final stage it can wait at the side of the stove without harm.

bouquet garni, or a few herbs tied in a bundle, or a pinch of mixed dried herbs

White Turnips and Carrots Cooked in Butter

Peel the turnips and scrape the carrots and cut them into large dice. Melt the butter in a pan and tip in the vegetables. Cover, and cook over a low heat for 30–35 minutes, stirring or shaking the pan occasionally. Season with a little salt and pepper and serve.

2 small turnips
2 medium carrots
1 oz butter or margarine

Pan Potatoes

Peel the potatoes and leave in cold water. Peel and chop the onion. Heat the butter in a large frying pan, add the onion and stir. Then cover the pan and cook until the onion is soft, but not brown. Add the flour and stir until well blended; add the milk, enough to cover the onion and cook until the mixture thickens. Dice the raw potatoes and heap them on top of the onion mixture. Cover the pan and cook very slowly for about 1 hour. To serve, chop across with a wooden spoon and stir before tipping into a warm dish. A sprinkling of chopped parsley is a nice finish, if you have any.

3 or 4 medium sized potatoes
1 small onion, or 1 shallot
1 oz butter or margarine
$\frac{1}{2}$ level tablespoon flour
about $\frac{1}{4}$ pint milk
1 teaspoon chopped parsley
(optional)

Prune Mousse

Soak the prunes overnight in plenty of cold tea. Next day place the prunes in a saucepan with $\frac{1}{4}$ pint of the tea used for soaking and 1 or 2 strips of pared lemon rind. Simmer until tender – about 15–20 minutes. Draw off the heat, add the sugar, stir to dissolve and then strain the juice from the prunes and set aside; if necessary make up to $\frac{1}{4}$ pint with a little water.

$\frac{1}{4}$ lb prunes
cold tea (see recipe)
rind and juice of $\frac{1}{2}$ lemon
1 oz sugar
3 tablespoons water
2 level teaspoons powdered gelatine
5 fl oz heavy (double) cream – see recipe
1 egg white

Remove the stones from the prunes and rub through a sieve or fine Mouli with the reserved liquid. Stir in the strained lemon juice. Measure the cold water into a small pan and sprinkle in the gelatine. Allow to soak for 5 minutes, then stir over a low heat to dissolve. Add the gelatine to the prune purée, pouring it in a thin, steady stream; stir well all the time to blend the mixture evenly. Allow to cool for a few minutes, then lightly whip the cream with very little milk to rinse out the carton. Take four heaped tablespoons from the whipped cream and fold into the fruit purée. Whisk the egg white until stiff and fold into the mixture with a metal spoon. Turn into a serving dish and chill for several hours. Scrape the remaining whipped cream into a tiny bowl or ramekin dish, and keep chilled to serve with black coffee.

THE LOVER IN A HURRY

Mushroom Consommé
Chicken in Paprika Cream Sauce
Rice or Noodles
Vanilla Ice Cream with Black Cherries

The mushroom consommé is an amazingly quick recipe to prepare, but makes a warming prelude to a winter evening. You can get everything ready for the chicken in about 10 minutes, then, leaving the dish to cook gently for half an hour or so, turn your attention to setting the table and getting yourself ready. No separate vegetable dish is needed, since there are tomatoes, onion and pimento with the chicken, but a dish of rice or noodles would go well with it. We have chosen a vanilla ice cream with black cherries for a dessert, so there is no cooking involved. But try to get a *real* dairy ice cream and a good quality can of cherries; some brands are ready-stoned, and a dash of brandy or cherry brandy liqueur would make them and the ice cream very special. If you can spare the time to heat the cherries in a pan before serving, they are simply delicious hot with the ice cream. Dark green candles, with a little garland of ivy round the base of the candlesticks, would look attractive without taking long to arrange.

Mushroom Consommé

Melt the butter in a saucepan. Peel and chop the onion. Add to the pan and sauté gently to soften but not brown. Add the washed, trimmed and thinly sliced mushrooms, cover and sauté gently for 3–4 minutes until the juices run out. Stir in the stock and bring nearly to the boil. Remove from the heat and add the sherry before serving.

$\frac{1}{2}$ oz butter
$\frac{1}{2}$ small onion or
1 shallot
$\frac{1}{4}$ lb button mushrooms
1 pint chicken stock
(made with bouillon cube)
1–2 tablespoons sherry

Chicken in Paprika Cream Sauce

Trim the chicken joints. Peel and slice the onion, quarter the tomatoes and discard the seeds. Melt the butter in a saucepan and brown the chicken joints on all sides, lift out and fry the onion in the saucepan until soft. Stir in the paprika and the wine. Simmer for a few minutes to reduce the liquid, then add the tomato. Cut the pimentos into neat strips and add to the contents in the pan. Season with salt, cover with a lid, and cook gently for 30–40 minutes. Lift out the chicken joints, or if using a whole chicken, carve the bird and reserve the best pieces. Put all the contents of the pan through a fine sieve or Mouli; at this stage the purée and the chicken may be kept warm in the pan, and reheated at the last moment. For the sauce, melt the butter in a small pan, stir in the flour and blend well, then stir in the top of milk, or cream, simmer for a minute or two, then dish the chicken. Stir the sauce into the puréed vegetables, and spoon over the chicken.

4 chicken portions, fresh not frozen
1 small onion
½ lb tomatoes, or
small tin tomatoes
1 oz butter
1 heaped teaspoon paprika
2 tablespoons dry white wine
2 caps pimento
salt
For the sauce
small nut butter
½ tablespoon flour
2 tablespoons
creamy milk, or thin cream

Rice or Noodles

Allow 3 oz rice or ribbon noodles for two people. Tip either into a pan of boiling salted water, stir and cook the rice for 12 minutes or the noodles for 15–20 according to the package. Drain the noodles through a colander, then return them to a clean pan in which you have melted a knob of butter. Cover the pan and draw off the heat. When ready to serve, reheat and turn with a wooden spoon to coat well with butter. For the rice, tip into wire strainer and wash well under hot water until the water runs clear. Drain. Heat a knob of butter in a clean pan and tip in the rice. Cover the pan and draw off the heat. When ready to serve, reheat and stir gently with a wooden spoon.

3 oz long grain rice or
3 oz ribbon noodles
water, see recipe
butter, see recipe

Vanilla Ice Cream with Black Cherries

Scoop two helpings of ice cream into a glass bowl. Tip the cherries into a basin and stir in the liqueur; spoon the cherries round the ice cream and trickle some juice over the top. If you are serving the cherries hot, heat them with the liqueur in a small pan, and serve them separately.

1 large block vanilla ice cream
1 small can black cherries
1 tablespoon brandy or cherry brandy (optional)

THE LOVER WITH TIME TO SPARE

Eggplant (Aubergine) Pâté
Doepeaza Dilaee Khanee
Rice
Fresh Fruit in Tangerine Cream

The time you spend on this menu will be fully justified by your reputation as a discerning and talented cook. The eggplant (aubergine) pâté is an unusual start to the meal, and is rich without being filling. The main dish is taken from an Indian recipe of the nineteenth century; the spices give it a faint and subtle hint of curry, while the creamy sauce, flavored with onions and almonds, adds a marvelous taste and texture. The whole dish can keep warm without spoiling, and you add the ground almonds and cream just before serving. For a dessert, fresh fruit is covered with a tangerine-flavored mousse-like cream and really will bring compliments to the chef.

To underline the taste of the dessert, put a small dish of tangerines on the table, and tuck some shiny evergreen leaves among them. Dark green or tangerine-colored candles would look very pretty.

Eggplant (Aubergine) Pâté

Place the eggplants (aubergines) in a roasting pan. Set in the center of a hot oven (400°F, 200°C or Gas No 6) and bake for 30–40 minutes, turning occasionally. The eggplants (aubergines) will feel soft when ready. Take out of the oven and when cool enough to handle, cut in half lengthwise and scoop out the soft flesh into a mixing basin. Mash with a fork, season with salt and pepper and beat in the lemon juice. Gradually beat in the oil. The resulting mixture should be quite thick. Lastly, beat in a small piece of crushed garlic to taste. Spoon into a small pot and chill until ready to serve.

Serve with hot toast.

If you want to use an electric blender, after baking, scoop the pulp from the eggplants into the container and add the lemon juice. Cover and blend until smooth. Then, on low speed, blend in the oil and garlic.

1 large or 2 small eggplants (aubergines)
salt
freshly milled pepper
1 tablespoon lemon juice
1½ tablespoons oil
small piece crushed garlic

Doepeaza Dilaee Khanee

Trim the meat and cut into thin slices. Crush the cloves and cardamom seeds and place in a basin with the pepper, cinnamon and turmeric. Stir in the sour cream mixed with the milk and blend well. Add the slices of meat and turn them in the mixture to coat well.

Heat a little more than half the clarified butter in a large saucepan. Add the pieces of meat and fry gently to brown on both sides. Pour the warm water into the bowl which contained the spice and sour cream mixture, stir well to blend in any remaining mixture and then pour over the meat in the saucepan. Cover with a lid and simmer gently over low heat for 1 hour.

Peel and thinly slice the large onion. Fry gently in the remaining clarified butter until tender and golden brown. Stir in the infused saffron, set aside. Peel the small onions and prick them all over with a fork. Rub them well with ground salt crystals. Remove the lid from the pan of meat and add the whole onions. Allow to simmer gently, uncovered, for a further 30 minutes or until the meat is tender.

Have ready the ground almonds and cream in a small bowl or cup. Before serving take out 4 tablespoons of the cooking liquid from the meat and blend it with the cream and almonds; pour over the meat and add the fried onion and saffron mixture.

Serve hot with rice as an accompaniment, see previous menu.

$\frac{3}{4}$ lb lean stewing beef
6 cloves
3 cardamom seeds
freshly milled pepper
$\frac{1}{2}$ level teaspoon ground cinnamon
1 level teaspoon ground turmeric
1 level tablespoon sour cream mixed with 1 tablespoon milk
3 oz clarified butter
$\frac{1}{4}$ pint warm water
1 small onion
pinch of saffron strands, soaked in 2 tablespoons hot water
4 small whole onions
salt – see recipe
1 oz ground almonds
1 tablespoon cream

Fresh Fruit in Tangerine Cream

Wash and dry the tangerines and rub the skins all over with the lumps of sugar to absorb the zest. Squeeze the juice from the tangerines, strain and set aside. Crush the sugar lumps and stir into 2 tablespoons of the juice until it dissolves. Put the granulated sugar and water into a small pan, slowly bring to the boil and stir to dissolve the sugar. Then boil steadily for 7 minutes. Take off the heat and cool. Place the egg yolks into a basin and set over a pan of simmering water; pour the sugar syrup slowly onto the yolks, whisking until the mixture thickens. Take off the heat and continue to whisk until the mixture is cold. Stir in the tangerine syrup and set in a cool place.

Peel, core and quarter the pears, and slice each quarter again in half. Peel and slice the banana lengthways into 4, then across to make inch-long strips. Place in a glass serving dish and pour the remaining tangerine juice over the fruit. Cover with a plate and keep chilled. Whip the cream lightly and fold into the tangerine sauce, keep chilled until ready. Pour over the fruit and serve.

2 tangerines
4 lumps of sugar
2 tablespoons sugar
2 tablespoons water
2 egg yolks
2 ripe dessert pears
1 banana
$\frac{1}{4}$ pint heavy (double) cream

February

THE AFFLUENT LOVER

Smoked Salmon, Brown Bread and Butter
Chicken Véronique
Green Salad
Fresh Fruit Salad

Smoked salmon is a luxurious beginning to any meal. Follow it with Chicken Véronique with a wine-flavored sauce and garnish of grapes. It is served on its own bed of pan-cooked potatoes, so no extra cooked vegetables are needed. A green salad of lettuce and watercress or lettuce and cucumber is a perfect accompaniment. Fresh fruit salad, with or without cream, completes the dinner, which is light and refreshing and not too rich. Choose a good Hock (Kabinett or Spätlese) and serve it chilled.

Smoked Salmon

Divide salmon between two plates, and serve with lemon wedges and thin slices of brown bread and butter, and a grinding of black pepper.

4 oz sliced smoked salmon
1 lemon
brown bread
butter
black pepper

Chicken Véronique

Set the chicken in a roasting pan and spread the breast of the chicken with butter. Put the tarragon, salt and pepper inside the bird and pour half the stock round it. Cover with foil and set in preheated oven (375°F, 190°C or Gas No 5) for about 1 hour.

Meanwhile, peel and finely slice the potatoes and pat dry. Spread the butter over an ovenproof serving dish which has a well-fitting lid, arrange the potato slices in it neatly and sprinkle with salt. Press a piece of buttered greaseproof paper over the potatoes and put on the lid. Cook in the oven for about ¾ hour.

Carve the chicken and arrange the best pieces on top of the potatoes, re-cover and keep warm. Strain the pan juices into a small saucepan, tip the wine into the roasting pan and boil up on top of the stove, stirring round with a wooden spoon to loosen the savory scrapings. When the wine has slightly reduced, pour into the saucepan and add the remaining stock and the flour mixed with water. Bring slowly to the boil, stirring well until

1 small roasting chicken
2 oz butter
½ teaspoon dried tarragon
½ teaspoon salt
pinch of pepper
¼ pint chicken stock made from the giblets or bouillon cube
2 medium potatoes
½ oz butter
½ teaspoon salt
2 tablespoons white wine
1 teaspoon flour, mixed with
1 tablespoon cold water
2 tablespoons cream
12 green grapes
½ lemon

the sauce thickens smoothly, then set aside. Peel and pip the grapes, put in a small cup and squeeze over the juice of $\frac{1}{2}$ a lemon and cover with a saucer.

To serve, heat the sauce and add the cream, then the grapes. Pour over the chicken and serve with a green salad tossed in a French dressing.

1 dessert apple
1 ripe pear
$\frac{1}{4}$ lb grapes
1 banana
1 orange

Fresh Fruit Salad

Prepare the syrup first and allow it to cool before adding the fruit. Measure the sugar and water into a small pan. Stir over low heat until the sugar has dissolved. Bring up to the boil and simmer for 3 minutes. Draw the pan off the heat, add the strained lemon juice and pour into a basin. Leave to cool, then add the Kirsch or brandy.

Peel, quarter and slice the apple and pear. Halve and de-seed the grapes, and peel and slice the banana. Using a sharp knife, cut away the outer peel from the orange and remove the orange sections individually. Each fruit should be added to the syrup as it is prepared, to prevent it discoloring. Stir and chill for several hours before serving.

For the syrup
2 oz sugar
2 tablespoons water
1 tablespoon lemon juice
1 tablespoon Kirsch or brandy
(optional)

THE IMPECUNIOUS LOVER

Casserole of Ox Kidney
Red Cabbage with Apple
Hot Bread Rolls
Caramel Custard

Make the caramel custard the evening before and an hour or so before you are ready to dine, loosen the top edges with a knife and turn the bowl upside down onto a serving dish; don't lift the bowl off until you are ready to eat. The savory casserole of ox kidney is warming and economical. Served with spicy red cabbage it is delicious; both will keep warm for ages. Pop the bread rolls into the oven for a few minutes to heat, or simply sit them on top of one of the saucepans on a plate to keep warm. They are good for mopping up the rich gravy. If you can manage a bottle of red wine, you should open it and leave it for an hour or so to acquire room temperature. The whole meal could be eaten in front of the fire on a sofa, or on the floor. A fork for the first course and a small spoon for the cool caramel custard is all you need. There is no table to set, no special flowers to arrange. Perhaps a little sweet background music would encourage a romantic atmosphere.

Casserole of Ox Kidney

Remove any fat or gristle from the kidney and cut into small pieces. Peel and finely chop the onion. Scrape and thinly slice the carrot. Melt the dripping in a heavy pan and, when hot, fry the onion and carrot until beginning to brown. Add the pieces of kidney and turn them to fry on all sides. Stir in the curry powder and the chutney, and then add enough stock to cover. Season with salt and pepper, and ginger if desired. Cover the pan and cook over a low heat for $1\frac{1}{4}$–$1\frac{1}{2}$ hours. It will not hurt to leave the pan over a very low heat for longer but add a little more stock if it tends to look dry.

8 oz ox kidney
2 small or 1 large onion
1 carrot
1 tablespoon dripping
$\frac{1}{2}$ tablespoon curry powder
1 rounded tablespoon chutney
$\frac{1}{4}$–$\frac{1}{2}$ pint stock to cover
salt and pepper
1 rounded teaspoon ground ginger (optional)

Red Cabbage with Apple

Cut the cabbage into quarters, slice away the center core and shred the cabbage finely. Melt the butter in a large saucepan. Peel and chop the onion. Add the onion and fry gently until soft, then add the red cabbage. Peel, core and chop the apple; add to the pan and pour in enough boiling water to cover the base of the saucepan to a depth of half an inch. Add the vinegar and sugar. Cover with a lid and bring up to the boil. Simmer gently for about 1 hour or until the cabbage and apples are tender. Stir the cabbage occasionally during the cooking and add a little extra water if necessary, but the mixture should not be too moist. Season with salt and pepper and serve nice and hot.

$\frac{1}{2}$ small red cabbage
$\frac{1}{2}$ oz butter
$\frac{1}{2}$ onion
1 cooking apple
water
1 tablespoon vinegar
$\frac{1}{2}$ tablespoon sugar
$\frac{1}{2}$ tablespoon sugar
$\frac{1}{2}$ teaspoon salt and pepper

Caramel Custard

First prepare the caramel. Measure 2 tablespoons of the sugar into a dry saucepan and place over a moderate heat. Leave until the sugar melts and turns golden brown, then remove from the heat. Pour at once into an ungreased 1 pint basin or ring mold. Holding the basin or mold in a cloth, tip about so that the caramel coats the inside. Leave to cool and set.

Break the eggs into a mixing basin, add the remaining sugar and whisk together lightly. Heat the milk to near boiling and pour onto the eggs and sugar. Strain the mixture into a jug and then pour into the mold containing the caramel. Stand the mold in a shallow baking tin containing an inch of cold water. Place in the center of a slow oven (300°F, 150°C or Gas No 2) and bake for 1 hour. Leave until cold before serving.

Loosen the top edges of the custard with a knife and invert over a glass dish. When ready to eat, lift away the mold.

3 level tablespoons sugar
2 eggs
$\frac{1}{2}$ pint milk

THE LOVER IN A HURRY

Grapefruit with Crème de Menthe
Noodles with Cream and Bacon Sauce
Tomato Salad
Glazed Peaches with Brown Sugar and Spice

If you do things in the following order the meal is very quick to prepare. Prepare the grapefruit and leave it to chill; it has a marvelously refreshing peppermint flavor. Then prepare the noodles, which take only 15 minutes to cook from start to finish, but leave out the egg yolk and cream until just before you are ready to eat. Have the yolk and cream mixed together in a coffee cup and then stir into the pan of noodles at the last moment, reheat, dish up and sprinkle with grated Parmesan. As you are using dry white wine in the recipe, you can recork and keep the bottle chilled until you are ready to drink it. Assemble the tomato salad, and finally prepare the peaches. Have them ready in the ovenproof dish and the sugar and spices already mixed in a small basin. All the dishes are attractively colored and suggest very much more time and trouble than they take to prepare.

Grapefruit with Crème de Menthe

Cut the grapefruit in half and loosen and separate the segments, removing any pips and pith. Sprinkle each half with sugar and carefully pour a tablespoon of crème de menthe into each grapefruit half. Chill until ready to serve.

1 grapefruit
1 tablespoon sugar
2 tablespoons crème de menthe

Noodles with Cream and Bacon Sauce

Add the noodles to a large pan of boiling salted water. Cook until tender for about 12 minutes, then drain.

Meanwhile, trim and chop the bacon and fry without extra fat. When just beginning to get crisp, sprinkle the bacon with freshly ground black pepper and stir in the wine. Add the cooked noodles, stir and heat gently. Draw the pan off the heat and add the egg yolk mixed with the cream. Turn the bacon and noodles over in the cream mixture. Check seasoning. Turn into a hot dish and sprinkle with grated Parmesan cheese.

4–6 oz ribbon noodles, green or plain
4 strips (rashers) bacon
freshly milled black pepper
4 tablespoons dry white wine
1 egg yolk
4 tablespoons cream
grated Parmesan cheese

Tomato Salad

Plunge the tomatoes into boiling water for a few seconds, then drain and remove the skins. Slice the tomatoes into a small shallow dish, season with a good pinch of salt and plenty of black pepper. Place the sugar, oil and vinegar in a small cup, stir well and then pour over the tomatoes. Scatter a little basil over the top and serve.

4 tomatoes
salt and pepper
1 teaspoon sugar
pinch of dried basil
2 tablespoons olive oil
$\frac{1}{2}$ tablespoon wine vinegar

Glazed Peaches with Brown Sugar and Spice

Drain the peaches and reserve the juice. Arrange the peach halves in an ovenproof dish. Mix the sugar and spices together in a small basin and sprinkle over the peaches. Pour about 4 tablespoons of the juice from the can round the peaches. When you start the meal, slip the dish into a moderately hot oven (375°F, 190°C or Gas No 5) and cook for about 15 minutes. Serve the peaches bubbling, hot and shiny, with chilled cream if desired.

1 small can peach halves (not slices)
1 heaped tablespoon brown sugar
$\frac{1}{2}$ level teaspoon ground cinnamon
$\frac{1}{4}$ teaspoon ground ginger
cream (optional)

THE LOVER WITH TIME TO SPARE

Vichyssoise
Sweetbread Flan
Creamed Spinach
Chocolate and Orange Mousse

Vichyssoise may be served either hot or cold, but during the winter months it is nicest hot. The sweetbread flan is delicious eaten warm, so you can prepare the flan case in advance; fill with the sweetbread mixture before your light of love is due to arrive, cover with a piece of buttered foil and keep in a just warm oven until you are ready. The spinach can be made hot in a matter of moments if left at the back of the stove until needed. The mousse has a wonderful flavor – dark, rich chocolate with the tang of oranges; it can be made the day before, or in the morning.

An ideal wine for this menu would be a Chinon, perhaps the rosé; but beware lest more be read into your choice than you intended, for the good St. Lovans used to recommend the wines of Chinon as a cure for impotence.

Vichyssoise

Trim the green tops of the leeks and reserve a little of the best green. Slice away the roots, slice the leeks through the center and then wash thoroughly. Shred the leeks finely, and peel and chop the onions.

Melt the butter in a large saucepan, add the vegetables and sauté gently in the covered pan for about 10 minutes until soft, but not brown. Peel and dice the potatoes and add to the pan, cook for a further 5 minutes, then stir in the hot stock and seasoning. Bring to the boil, then simmer gently for 30–40 minutes. Remove the pan from the heat and pass the vegetables and liquid through a sieve or Mouli, or purée the soup in an electric blender; stir in the cream. Check the seasoning and serve hot with a little of the reserved green part of the leeks, cut very finely, sprinkled on each bowl.

½ lb leeks
1 onion
1 oz butter
6 oz potatoes
1 pint chicken stock
½ teaspoon salt
freshly milled pepper
2 tablespoons cream

Sweetbread Flan

Sift together flour and salt. Measure the fat onto a plate. Using a knife blade, mix the fats until soft and blended. Add to the flour and rub in evenly. It is important not to overmix the pastry and rubbing in should stop when the mixture looks crumbly.

Add all the water at once to the mixture. Stir with a fork, until the mixture clings together in a ball, leaving the basin sides clean. Turn the dough on to a lightly floured surface, and knead lightly to make a smooth, fairly stiff dough. Set the pastry to rest before using.

Roll out the pastry on a lightly floured surface to a circle slightly larger than a 6-inch flan ring or shallow cake tin. Grease the ring and line with pastry; trim the edges. Fill the center of the flan with a piece of crumpled kitchen foil to keep the shape while baking. Bake in the center of a hot oven (400°F, 200°C or Gas No 6) for 10–12 minutes. Remove the foil 2 or 3 minutes before the end of the cooking time. Set the pastry case aside while preparing the filling.

Soak the sweetbreads in several changes of cold water for an hour or more. Put them into a saucepan with enough cold water to cover them, bring slowly to the boil and cook for 10 minutes. Drain the sweetbreads and, when cool enough to handle, remove any fat or dark skin; put them between two plates with a weight on top. Peel and chop the onion and put in a small pan of cold water, bring to the boil, then drain immediately. Drain the prunes from the liquid in which they soaked, stone and chop them into pieces.

Heat the butter in a pan, roll the sweetbreads in a little of the flour and fry them on each side until golden. Lift them out into an ovenproof dish and add the onion to the pan. When the onion begins to soften and turn yellow, add the prunes and gently turn together with a wooden spoon to cook for 2 or 3 minutes, then lift them from the pan and add to the dish of sweetbreads. Shake the rest of the flour into the pan and stir over a medium heat, slowly add the stock and the wine, stirring all the time until the sauce comes to the boil and thickens smoothly. Season with salt and pepper, and stir in the tarragon and parsley. Pour over the dish of sweetbreads, cover with a well-fitting lid or kitchen foil, and cook in the center of a moderately hot oven (375°F, 190°C or Gas No 5) for 35–40 minutes. If the sauce is not well reduced or thickened, remove the lid or foil for a further 10 minutes. Turn down the oven to the lowest setting. Allow the sweetbreads to cool a little, then spoon the mixture into the flan case, lay a piece of buttered foil on top and keep the dish warm in the oven with the door ajar or shut, depending on whether you eat sooner or later.

For the pastry case
3 oz flour
pinch of salt
1 oz butter
1 oz white vegetable fat
1 tablespoon water

Sweetbread and prune filling
½ lb sweetbreads
1 medium onion
4 large prunes soaked overnight
1 oz butter
½ oz flour
½ pint chicken stock
2 tablespoons red wine
½ teaspoon dried tarragon
1 tablespoon chopped fresh parsley
salt and pepper

Creamed Spinach

Wash the spinach and put in a large pan without water. Cover and bring to the boil; turn with a wooden spoon and cook for 10–15 minutes. Drain well through a colander, then pass through a sieve or food mill. Heat the butter in a pan and add the spinach. Stir over the heat until any surplus water has evaporated, then stir in the cream and season with a good grating of pepper and nutmeg if desired. Turn into a small ovenproof dish, cover and keep warm in the oven with the flan until needed.

1½ lbs spinach
1 oz butter
2 fl oz cream
freshly milled pepper
nutmeg if desired

Chocolate and Orange Mousse

Break the chocolate into a basin and add the water. Set over a pan of simmering water until the chocolate has melted. Squeeze the juice from the ½ orange and place in a small pan. Sprinkle in the gelatine and leave to soak for 5 minutes.

Separate the eggs, placing the yolks in one basin, the whites in another. Add the sugar to the yolks, set over a pan of hot water and whisk together until pale and thick. Remove from the heat and continue whisking until cool, then add the chocolate. Put the soaked gelatine over a low heat until it has dissolved – this will take only a few moments. Remove the pan from the heat and pour slowly into the chocolate mixture, stir to blend thoroughly and allow to cool and thicken, then fold in the stiffly beaten egg whites with a metal spoon. Pour into a glass or china serving dish.

3 oz plain chocolate
2 tablespoons water
½ orange
½ package powdered gelatine
2 eggs
1 rounded tablespoon sugar

March

THE AFFLUENT LOVER

Avocado Soup
Chicken with Foie Gras and Cream
Rice with Chicken Liver
Zucchini (Courgettes)
French Chocolate Ice Cream

The avocado soup is as pale and pretty as it is delicious. If made the day before it can be kept in the refrigerator in a plastic container with a lid. The chicken dish is both extravagant and subtle; if you keep it well covered and add the hot sauce when you are ready to eat, it will stay freshly flavored. Rice, too, is a good last-minute reheater, and the vegetables will not spoil if kept in the pan they were cooked in, and brought back to the simmer for a minute or two. After this, the wonderfully smooth, rich chocolate ice cream makes a lovely end to the meal. It will keep in the freezer compartment of the refrigerator for a week at least.

Avocado Soup

Halve the avocado and remove the stone. Scoop the flesh into an electric blender and add the chicken stock. Cover and blend for a few moments until smooth. Pour into a bowl and stir in the cream, lemon juice and salt and pepper to taste. Chill well, and stir in the chopped parsley before serving.

1 ripe avocado
¾ pint chicken stock
2 tablespoons cream
1 tablespoon lemon juice
salt and pepper
finely chopped parsley

Chicken with Foie Gras and Cream

Ask your butcher to joint the chicken. Trim the pieces neatly, removing the wing tips and back, but leave the skin on. Heat the oil and butter together in a large pan, and when sizzling, carefully put in the chicken pieces and brown on each side. Then season with salt and pepper, cover, and continue to cook over a low heat for 15 minutes. Add 2 tablespoons of the wine, re-cover the pan, and cook slowly for ½ an hour longer. Test a thigh joint with the point of a sharp knife and if the juices are clear, not pink, the chicken has cooked enough. Draw off the heat.

Put the stock and the rest of the wine into a small saucepan, stir in the arrowroot mixed with water and bring slowly to the

1 small roasting chicken (2½ lbs)
1 tablespoon oil
1 oz butter
½ teaspoon salt
freshly milled pepper
4 tablespoons white wine
2 fl oz chicken stock (made from giblets)
1 tablespoon arrowroot mixed with a little cold water
2 oz pâté de foie gras
3 tablespoons cream

boil, stirring until the sauce thickens. Mix the pâté with a spoonful or two of hot sauce in a small basin, then rub through a strainer and add to the pan. When ready to serve put the pan of chicken over a medium heat, stir the cream into the small pan of sauce and bring nearly to the boil. Dish the chicken joints and spoon the sauce over them.

Rice

(See p 48, January: Lover in a Hurry.) Save the chicken liver from the cooked giblets, chop finely and scatter over the dish of rice.

Zucchini (Courgettes)

Trim the zucchini and slice thickly. Add to a saucepan of boiling salted water. Bring to the boil and simmer for 2 minutes, then drain.

    Melt the butter in a large frying pan. Add the zucchini (courgettes), cover and sauté gently for about 15 minutes until soft. Draw off the heat. When ready to serve reheat for 2 or 3 minutes. Season with freshly milled pepper.

½ lb zucchini (courgettes)
1 oz butter
freshly milled pepper

French Chocolate Ice Cream

Break the chocolate into squares and put into the bowl of an electric mixer over a pan of hot water to soften a little. Put the sugar and water in a small saucepan, bring to the boil and keep stirring until the sugar dissolves, then boil fast for 3 minutes. Add the hot syrup to the bowl of chocolate and blend with the mixer until smooth. Add the egg yolks and blend again for a minute. Switch off. If the cream is very thick, rinse out the carton with a little milk and whisk together lightly. Fold the cream into the chocolate mixture, spoon into a small carton or tub, cover with the lid, or foil. Freeze. Transfer to the main part of the refrigerator at the beginning of the meal, so that it is not too hard when you serve it.

4 oz plain chocolate
1 rounded tablespoon sugar
3 tablespoons water
2 egg yolks
5 fl oz heavy (double) cream

THE IMPECUNIOUS LOVER

Chicory Salad with Orange
Smoked Fish Kedgeree
Rhubarb Charlotte

This is an easy and economical meal for two. When you are preparing the chicory and orange salad, grate the rind from the orange and save it for flavoring the rhubarb charlotte. It is more unusual than apple charlotte, and rhubarb is good at this time of year and a welcome change from winter desserts. The kedgeree is an ideal supper dish for lovers; it reheats good-naturedly however long you take to work up an appetite. A little jug of early daffodils set at the side of your table will be a harbinger of spring and romance.

Chicory Salad with Orange

Wash and trim the heads of chicory and then cut across into thick slices. Stir the chicory in the oil and vinegar dressing and spoon into a shallow bowl. Cut away the skin and white pith from the orange, using a sharp knife. Then cut out the sections of orange flesh, leaving the skin between the sections behind. Add the orange to the salad, toss and serve.

2 heads of chicory
2 tablespoons oil and vinegar dressing
1 small orange

Smoked Fish Kedgeree

Rinse the smoked fish and cut into large pieces. Put in a saucepan with $\frac{3}{4}$ pint of water to cover. Add the bay leaf, the $\frac{1}{2}$ lemon cut in slices (or the vinegar) and a few peppercorns. Bring to the boil, then lower the heat and simmer very gently until the fish is tender – about 10–15 minutes. Strain off the cooking liquid and reserve $\frac{1}{2}$ pint.

Melt $\frac{1}{2}$ oz butter in a pan. Peel and finely chop the onion. Add to the pan, cover with a lid and cook very gently for about 5 minutes until the onion is soft. Stir in the rice and then add the reserved fish liquid. Bring to the boil, stir and then lower the heat and cook until the rice is tender and the liquid absorbed; this takes about 20–30 minutes. Meanwhile remove any bones and skin from the cooked fish and break into flakes. Hard boil the eggs, then remove the shells and cut into quarters.

$\frac{3}{4}$ lb smoked cod, or
1 small smoked haddock on the bone
1 small bay leaf
$\frac{1}{2}$ lemon or 2 tablespoons vinegar
peppercorns
1 oz butter
4 oz long-grain rice
$\frac{1}{2}$ small onion
$\frac{1}{2}$ pint cooking liquid from fish
2 eggs
freshly milled pepper

Using a fork, fold these and the remaining butter cut in small pieces into the cooked rice; check the seasoning, using plenty of pepper. Set aside, and when needed reheat until nice and hot.

Rhubarb Charlotte

Put the breadcrumbs, sugar and suet into a small basin, and set aside.

Wash and trim the rhubarb, and cut into 1-inch lengths. Place in a saucepan with the butter, cover with a lid and stew very gently until the rhubarb is quite soft – about 5–10 minutes. Beat in the sugar and grated orange rind and draw off the heat.

Butter a 1 pint baking dish, and tip in two-thirds of the crumb mixture. Press over the base and sides of the dish. Pour in the rhubarb mixture and top with the rest of the crumb mixture. Sprinkle with Demerara sugar, and dot with small flakes of butter. Place in the center of a moderately hot oven (375°F, 190°C or Gas No 5) and bake for about 35–40 minutes, or until crisp and golden brown. Lay a piece of foil over the charlotte, switch off the oven, and leave the door ajar until ready to eat. Serve with top of milk or cream.

2 oz fresh white breadcrumbs
1 oz sugar
1 oz shredded suet
$\frac{1}{2}$ lb rhubarb
$\frac{1}{2}$ oz butter
1 oz sugar grated rind of orange (left from orange and chicory salad)

For the topping
1 level tablespoon Demerara sugar
1 small pat of butter

THE LOVER IN A HURRY

Scallops with Cream
Lamb Cutlets in Mushroom and Sherry Sauce
Bananas with Stem Ginger and Ice Cream

For a dinner that has been arranged at short notice this menu suggests that you are a cook of sheer genius; yet the time spent in cooking and preparing the dishes is only about half an hour.

The best order in which to tackle the menu is to prepare the lamb cutlets first and put them to soak in the sherry. Peel the mushrooms and trim the scallops. Chop the ginger for the ice cream and let it soak in its syrup in a small bowl. Then cook the lamb dish, and keep it warm in a gentle oven. When you are ready to eat, the scallops are cooked in 5 minutes under the admiring gaze of your lover. And, at the end of the meal, the delicious banana ice cream is assembled in a matter of moments. Eating in a warm and tidy kitchen would give an atmosphere of cozy intimacy and save time in carrying dishes and table settings to another room. Afterwards, you can sink together into the deepest armchair for coffee and a liqueur to reward you for your skill in the kitchen.

Scallops with Cream

Rinse and slice the scallops into two or three pieces. Heat the butter in a pan and, when frothing, add the scallops. Sauté gently, turning once or twice, for about 5 minutes. Draw off the heat. When ready to serve season to taste, reheat gently and stir in the cream when hot but not boiling.

4 fresh scallops
1 oz butter
salt and pepper
2 fl oz cream

Lamb Cutlets in Mushroom and Sherry Sauce

Cut the little round nut of meat from each cutlet, place in a small basin and pour over the sherry. Take the 4 largest mushroom caps and peel them carefully. Peel the rest of the mushrooms, and make up the stock with boiling water and half a bouillon cube. Heat the butter in a pan. Lift the pieces of meat from the basin, reserving the sherry. Sauté them for about 4 minutes on each side until brown, lift out and set aside. Sauté

4 lamb cutlets from the best end of neck
2 tablespoons sherry
½ lb mushrooms
2 fl oz stock (4 tablespoons)
½ oz butter
salt and pepper
French loaf, or mashed potatoes

the four large mushrooms quickly on each side and place them in the center of a warm serving dish. Sauté the rest of the mushrooms.

Arrange each nut of lamb on a large mushroom, surround with the remaining mushrooms and keep warm. Add the stock and sherry from the basin to the pan, season with a little salt and pepper and bring to the boil, stirring all the time. When boiling, pour over the lamb and serve with French bread, or, if you prefer and have time, mashed potatoes.

Bananas with Ginger and Ice Cream

Chop the stem ginger and put in a small basin with the syrup. When ready to serve, peel the bananas and slice them into the basin of ginger. Put a scoop of ice cream onto each plate and spoon the bananas and ginger on top.

2 bananas
1 tablespoon chopped stem ginger
4 tablespoons syrup from stem ginger
2 scoops of good vanilla ice cream

THE LOVER WITH TIME TO SPARE

Mushroom Cocktail
Mexican Chicken with Sweet Corn
Green Peppers Stuffed with Rice
Cold Lemon Soufflé

Nearly all the cooking can be done in advance. The lemon soufflé can be made the day before, and the mushroom cocktail a few hours before dinner. The stuffed peppers and ingredients for the Mexican chicken can be prepared well in advance. Both should start on their final cooking about an hour before you expect to eat, but if your appetite for the loved one delays that of the gourmet, then keep the peppers covered in a gentle oven and, when ready to serve, thicken the chicken sauce with the nut of butter kneaded with flour, draw the pan over a medium heat and stir as you bring to the simmer. Dish the stuffed peppers by which time the chicken will have heated through. They combine to make a spicy, exotic dish. The cool, creamy mushrooms are very delicate and appetizing as a starter and, to finish the meal, the billowy lemon soufflé is as unsubstantial as a dream.

An excellent, though unusual wine to accompany this menu would be an Italian Soave, or, perhaps better still, a Hungarian Mori Ezerjó.

Mushroom Cocktail

Wash the mushrooms and remove the stalks. Halve or quarter any large ones. Place in a small saucepan, just cover with cold water, add a pinch of salt and a small nut of butter. Bring to the boil, cover and simmer gently for 5 minutes, or until tender. Drain the mushrooms and chill. Continue to cook the liquid until reduced to less than a tablespoonful and allow to cool.

Wash and shred the lettuce leaves and arrange in the bottom of individual glass dishes. Combine together the ingredients for the dressing, then fold in the chilled mushrooms. Pile into the glasses and sprinkle the top of each with a pinch of paprika.

4 oz button mushrooms
cold water
pinch of salt
butter
2–3 lettuce leaves
paprika

For the dressing
2 tablespoons mayonnaise
2 tablespoons thick cream
½ tablespoon reduced mushroom liquid
½ teaspoon horseradish sauce
dash Worcestershire sauce
squeeze of lemon juice

Mexican Chicken with Sweet Corn

Trim the chicken joints neatly. Heat the butter in a large pan and sauté the chicken until golden brown on each side.

Halve the pepper and remove the seeds, then shred finely. Drain the sweet corn. Peel and slice the onion and put with the pepper in a pan of cold water. Bring to the boil and then drain. Using about two-thirds of the sweet corn, mix all the vegetables together and tip them into a large pan. Arrange the chicken joints on top, and season with salt and pepper. Pour over just enough stock to cover the chicken, cover the pan tightly and cook gently for about ¾ hour, until the chicken is tender. Add a squeeze of lemon juice and the chopped parsley. Draw off the heat. To thicken, drop in a little nut of butter kneaded with flour, then reheat when ready to serve.

4 chicken joints
1 oz butter
1 large green pepper
1 small can sweet corn
1 small onion thinly sliced
¼ pint chicken stock, made from the giblets
squeeze of lemon juice
1 tablespoon chopped parsley
small amount of flour
butter

Green Peppers Stuffed with Rice

Carefully cut a circle from the stalk end of each pepper and scoop out the seeds. Wash and turn upside-down to drain. Peel and finely chop the onion. Heat the oil in a pan and soften the onion in it until turning yellow. Add the crushed garlic, stir, and draw off the heat. Skin the tomatoes and chop them roughly, discarding the seeds; add them to the contents of the pan, with a seasoning of salt, then stir in the cooked rice. Mix well and stuff the peppers with this mixture. Set in a small tin with a little chicken stock. Cover with foil and cook in oven (375°F, 190°C or Gas No 5) for about an hour.

2 small green peppers
1 medium onion
2 tablespoons oil
1 clove garlic
2 tomatoes
½ teaspoon salt
1 cup cooked rice
2 or 3 tablespoons chicken stock

Lemon Soufflé

Separate the eggs and put the yolks in a warm basin with the sugar, the grated rind and strained juice of the lemon. Stand the basin over a pan of simmering water and whisk until mixture is pale and light. Take the basin from the pan and put it on a damp cloth, then whisk for 5 minutes. Sprinkle the gelatine on to the cold water in a small saucepan. When it is spongy, set the pan over a low heat until the gelatine has dissolved and the liquid is clear. Remove from the heat and allow to cool a little,

2 small eggs
3 oz sugar
1 large or 2 small lemons
half package powdered gelatine (¼ oz)
2 tablespoons cold water
¼ pint heavy (double) cream

then trickle the gelatine on to the egg and lemon mixture and whisk thoroughly. Lightly whip the cream, adding a little milk to the carton if it is very thick, and fold into the mixture. Finally, whisk the egg whites until stiff and fold them into the lemon mixture. Leave for about 15 minutes until the mixture begins to thicken, then pour into a small soufflé dish, or into individual glasses.

Ah, my Beloved, fill the Cup that clears
To-day of past Regrets and Future Fears:
Omar Khayyam

There will be work for questing hands   Exploring those mysterious lands
And fingers will play their part   Where Cupid bathes his burning dart.   Ovid

What wond'rous life is this I lead!
Ripe apples drop about my head;
The luscious clusters of the vine
Upon my mouth do crush their wine;
The nectarine and curious peach,
Into my hands themselves do reach . . .
                    Andrew Marvell

O! beware my lord of jealousy;
It is the green-ey'd monster which doth mock
The meat it feeds on.
          William Shakespeare

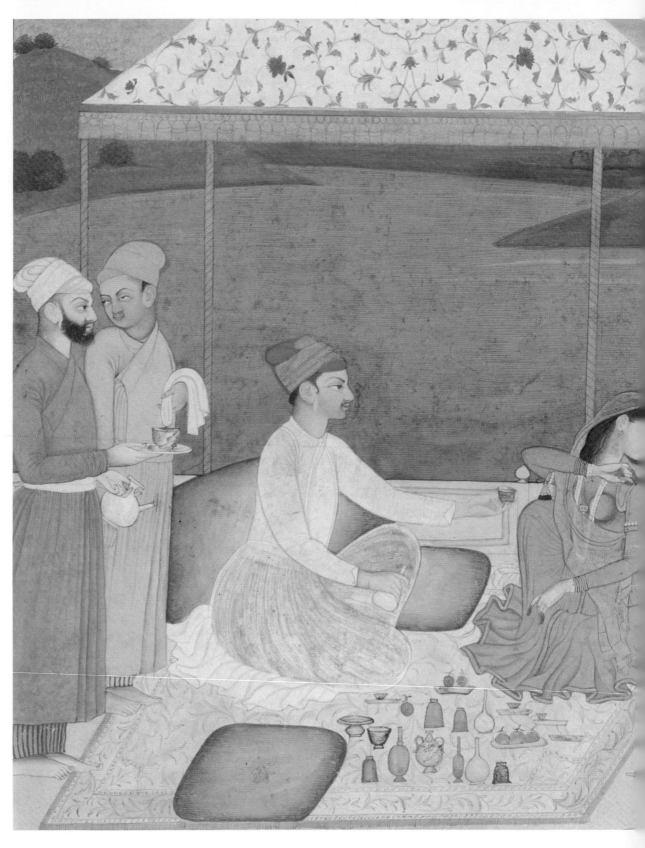

He brought me to the banqueting house, and his banner over me was love.

Song of Solomon

The thirst that from the soul doth rise
Doth ask a drink divine . . .

But might I of Jove's nectar sup,
I would not change for thine.
                    Ben Jonson

Come today, we will dine together: love has prepared entertainment for you all night.   Propertius

The place for love is a boudoir
Where garish day is left behind
With sofas soft and close-shut door
And light dim filtered through a blind,
The shade a decent veil will throw
And hide what 'tis not fit to show.

Ovid

License my roving hands, and let them go
Before, behind, between, above, below.
John Donne

They eat, they drink and in communion
Sweet, quaff immortality and joy.
                    John Milton

Nothing we see but means our good,
As our delight or as our treasure;
The whole is either our cupboard of food
Or cabinet of pleasure.
        George Herbert

The first night of my happiness is close at hand: O moon, make the first night of my embraces longer . . . How many hours must I talk away before Venus prepares as delicious a warfare for me?

Propertius

There is an element of adventure in eating out of doors that is felt the world over. (The little elephant is made of pastry and used to be a favorite sweatmeat.)

Full nakedness, all joys are due to thee.
As souls unbodied, bodies unclothed must be,
To taste whole joys . . .

      John Donne

April

THE AFFLUENT LOVER

Smoked Salmon and Stuffed Eggs
Lamb Cutlets in Sweet-Sour Sauce
Green Beans
Mousse of Apricots with Apricot Syrup Sauce

The apricot dessert should be prepared the previous day, and the delicious smoked salmon with stuffed eggs can be made well in advance. Everything can be got ready for the dish of cutlets, and the casserole placed in the oven $1\frac{1}{2}$ hours before you want to eat; with the oven turned very low after $\frac{3}{4}$ hour, the dish could remain for 2 hours without harm in its rich and spicy gravy. Green beans are in the shops now and have much more flavor than frozen ones. They should be small and young, so they are quickly cooked to tender crispness.

Pink champagne would be a delicious extravagance, but it is rare, and a good sparkling rosé, nicely chilled, would also suit the reckless gaiety of a sweet spring evening. If you buy some sprays of lilac, you will find they are usually sold on long branches. Ruthlessly cut these to about 6 inches and arrange the short, fragrant bunch in a low bowl. Mingled shades of mauve, or pure white, are equally sentimental and charming.

Smoked Salmon and Stuffed Eggs

Plunge the eggs into a pan of cold water, bring to the boil and cook for 8 minutes. Then run cold water over them until quite cool. Cut the eggs in half lengthways and scoop out the yolks into a small basin. Add the softened butter and cream the yolks and butter together with a wooden spoon. Season lightly with salt and pepper and work in the chopped gherkin, or dill pickle. When smooth, add the cream and mix well together. Divide this mixture into four and refill the halved egg whites.

Trim the crusts from the bread and butter, cut the slices square and trim the smoked salmon to fit the bread. Serve each piece topped with a stuffed egg.

2 eggs
1 oz softened butter
salt and pepper
1 teaspoon finely chopped gherkin or dill pickle
$\frac{1}{2}$ tablespoon cream
3 or 4 oz smoked salmon
2 slices brown bread and butter

Lamb Cutlets in Sweet-Sour Sauce

Trim the fat from the cutlets. Heat the oil in a frying pan, and brown the cutlets on both sides. Trim and slice the mushrooms. Lift the cutlets from the pan and place in a small ovenproof dish with the mushrooms. Measure the red currant jelly, Worcestershire sauce and lemon juice into a small pan. Stir over low heat until the jelly has melted.

Add the flour to the hot fat remaining in the frying pan. Stir over a low heat until golden brown, then stir in the jelly mixture and enough stock to make a thick sauce. Bring to the boil, stirring all the time to blend the mixture evenly. Season with salt, pepper and nutmeg to taste. Strain the sauce over the cutlets, cover and place in a moderately slow oven (325°F, 170°C or Gas No 3) and cook for $1\frac{1}{2}$ hours.

4 lamb cutlets
1 tablespoon vegetable oil
2 oz mushrooms
2 tablespoons red currant jelly
1 tablespoon Worcestershire sauce
juice of $\frac{1}{2}$ lemon
$\frac{1}{2}$ level tablespoon flour
$\frac{1}{4}$ pint stock
salt
freshly milled pepper
grated nutmeg

Green Beans

Prepare the beans in advance and have ready a pan of simmering water. Cook for 8–10 minutes. Drain well, toss in butter and serve.

$\frac{1}{2}$ lb green beans
salt
small nut of butter

Mousse of Apricots with Apricot Syrup Sauce

Soak the apricots overnight. Put the apricots and their liquid in a small pan and cook gently until soft. Remove from heat and rub through a fine sieve or food-mill. Leave to cool. Heat the milk in a small pan until nearly boiling. Cream the egg yolks and sugar together in a basin, pour on the milk, stir, and then return to the pan and stir over a low heat until smoothly thickened but not boiling. Strain into a basin and set aside.

Put the lemon juice and cold water into a small pan, sprinkle on the gelatine and leave until spongy. Set the pan over a low heat until the gelatine has dissolved. Pour the gelatine onto the egg and milk mixture, stirring all the while. Leave to cool.

Measure two-thirds of the apricot purée into a basin. Lightly whip the cream and fold into the purée. When the egg mixture starts to thicken, fold in the apricot purée and cream. Turn into an oiled mold and allow to set.

Put the sugar and water into a small pan and bring slowly to the boil, stirring until the sugar has dissolved. Boil fast for 3 minutes, then draw off the heat. Cool before stirring into the remaining purée, then chill thoroughly. To serve, loosen the edges of the apricot mousse with the tip of a knife and turn onto a pretty dish. Pour round the chilled sauce.

3 oz dried apricots
water to cover
$\frac{1}{4}$ pint milk
2 egg yolks
2 oz sugar
1 rounded teaspoon gelatine
juice of $\frac{1}{2}$ lemon
1 tablespoon water
2 fl oz cream

For the syrup
$1\frac{1}{2}$ oz sugar
2 fl oz cold water

THE IMPECUNIOUS LOVER

Cream of Carrot Soup
Pressed Lambs' Tongues
Green Salad
Potatoes Normande
Lemon Whip

It is nice to start this otherwise cold menu with a hot soup which can be heated through whenever you are ready. The dish of oven-browned potatoes is mouth-wateringly good and so easy to prepare, but if you are reluctant to use the oven just for that, you could buy a nice crusty French loaf and serve it in thick slices with some butter. The lemon whip is really a cheating mousse, without the expense of cream; the small trouble of whisking it until on the point of setting gives wonderful volume and lightness to the dessert. An inexpensive white wine, or some well-chilled beer would suit the menu as well as your pocket.

Cream of Carrot Soup

Scrape and slice the carrots and peel and finely slice the onion.

Melt the butter in a saucepan and add the prepared vegetables. Sauté gently for 2–3 minutes, or until vegetables are softened slightly. Add the stock, made from two bouillon cubes, season with salt and pepper, stir well and bring to the boil. Cover with a lid and simmer gently for about 1 hour, until the vegetables are quite tender.

Remove the pan from the heat, and rub the soup through a sieve or Mouli. Return to the pan, check seasoning and reheat. Before serving stir in the cream.

½ lb carrots
1 medium onion
1 oz butter
1 pint chicken stock
salt
freshly milled pepper
2 fl oz light (single) cream

Pressed Lambs' Tongues

Trim the tongues, put in a pan and cover with cold water. Bring to the boil and blanch for 2 minutes. Rinse the tongues in a colander, then return to a clean pan with just enough water to cover them and the peeled onion and scraped carrot roughly chopped. Add the bay leaf, mace and salt, and cook gently for 1½ hours. Test the tongues with the point of a sharp knife; if it easily pierces the tips, they are cooked. Plunge into

4 lambs' tongues
cold water
½ onion
½ carrot
1 bay leaf
1 blade of mace
a tiny pinch of salt

cold water and, as soon as you can handle them, peel away the skin. Have ready two mugs and curl the tongues and press down two into each mug. Cover with a small saucer and put a weight on each. When quite cold, run a knife round the inside of the mug and turn out the tongues. They can be sliced and arranged on a bed of salad, or you can serve a tossed green salad separately.

Potatoes Normande

Peel and slice the potatoes into thin rounds. Pat them dry. Butter a small ovenproof dish and arrange the potatoes in layers, sprinkling a little salt and pepper between each layer. Pour over the milk and put a few flakes of butter on top. Cook in a preheated oven (375 °F, 190 °C or Gas No 5) for $1-1\frac{1}{4}$ hours, until the potatoes are brown and crisp on top and soft beneath.

$\frac{3}{4}$ lb potatoes
$\frac{1}{2}$ oz butter
salt and pepper
$\frac{1}{4}$ pint milk

Lemon Whip

Measure the water into a saucepan and sprinkle in the gelatine; allow to soak for 5 minutes. Add the sugar and grated rind of the lemon. Stir over a low heat until the sugar and gelatine have both dissolved. Draw off the heat and strain into a basin. Set aside until cold and on the point of setting. Then add the strained lemon juice and the unbeaten egg whites to the gelatine mixture and whisk until thick and white. When the mixture is fairly stiff, turn into a serving dish and chill until firm.

$\frac{1}{4}$ pint cold water
$\frac{1}{4}$ oz powdered gelatine
2 oz sugar
rind and juice of 1 lemon
2 egg whites

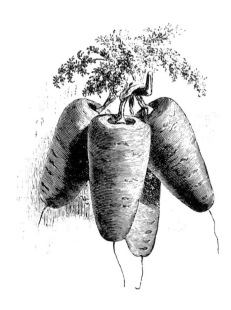

THE LOVER IN A HURRY

Avocado with Vinaigrette Dressing
Fillet Steak with Mustard Butter
Fried Tomatoes
Abricots Flambés

If the chance of an evening of delicious dalliance is sudden and unexpected, you can – provided the shops are still open – produce this well balanced and luxurious little dinner with the minimum of time and trouble.

The avocado must be sprinkled with lemon juice as soon as cut and destoned to prevent discoloring; otherwise it is ready in a jiffy and will wait with the vinaigrette dressing until you are ready. Make the mustard butter for the steak and leave it in the refrigerator; prepare the apricots (10 minutes) and leave at the side of the stove until you are ready to flame them in brandy – always an impressive piece of showmanship. Broil (grill) the steak and at the same time fry the tomatoes. Get the mustard butter out of the refrigerator and put a pat on each steak.

Choose a red and white checked cloth, a good but unpretentious claret or red Burgundy, French bread in a basket and, if you have time, a bunch of polyanthus. If you jam them into a small jar or jug, they arrange themselves, and look full of spring and hope.

Avocado with Vinaigrette Dressing

Halve the avocado and remove the stone. Squeeze lemon juice over all the cut surface. Put all the ingredients for the vinaigrette dressing into a small screw-top jar, and when ready to serve, shake well, and pour into the hollow of each avocado half. Serve the rest in a little jug.

1 avocado
lemon juice – see recipe
1 teaspoon French mustard
3 tablespoons olive oil
1 tablespoon white
wine vinegar
salt and pepper to taste

Fillet Steak with Mustard Butter

Brush the steaks over with oil and set under pre-heated broiler (grill). Broil (grill) for 5 minutes each side, or according to how rare or well-done you prefer.

Cream the butter in a small basin until softened. Add the mustard, parsley and a squeeze of lemon juice. Flatten the mixture level in basin and put into the refrigerator to chill. When ready to serve, cut two squares of mustard butter and put on top of each steak.

2 rounds fillet steak
oil for cooking

For the mustard butter
2 oz butter
½ teaspoon made mustard
1 tablespoon chopped
parsley

Fried Tomatoes

Wipe and halve tomatoes. Heat butter in a small frying pan until sizzling, but not brown. Sauté the tomatoes rounded side down for a minute, turn and sauté cut side down for another minute. Remove pan from heat, and when steaks are ready, serve the tomatoes on the same dish. Have some thick slices of a crusty French loaf ready to eat with this course.

4 tomatoes
1 oz butter

Abricots Flambés

Melt the butter in a frying pan and add the sugar. Using a wooden spoon, stir over heat until the sugar has melted and is an even golden brown. Add the orange juice and stir until the caramel melts into a syrup. Drain the apricots from their juice and add to the pan. Turn the apricots gently until they become glazed with syrup. At this stage the pan can be left at the back of the stove until needed. To finish, set the pan over the heat and when the apricots are hot, add brandy and flame. Remove pan from heat and pour on the cream. Stir to blend the sauce and serve hot.

$\frac{1}{2}$ oz butter
1 oz sugar
juice of $\frac{1}{2}$ orange
small can of apricot halves
1 tablespoon brandy
half a small carton of cream
($2\frac{1}{2}$ oz)

THE LOVER WITH TIME TO SPARE

Canneloni Stuffed with Savory Meat
Fresh Tomato Sauce
Galantine of Ham
Bean and Mushroom Salad
Fresh Pears in a Custard Cream

Although the menu takes a certain amount of time to prepare, everything can be made well in advance, and only the canneloni needs heating in the oven. You will have all the time you want for making your room look welcoming, the table intimate, or glamorous, with a flower arrangement that should be eye-catching without being large or obtrusive. Plenty of time, too, to make yourself look attractive, knowing that the kitchen work is over and the fun is about to begin.

Canneloni Stuffed with Savory Meat

First prepare the tomato sauce for the canneloni. It keeps in the refrigerator for a week, or indefinitely in the freezer. Heat the butter in a saucepan. Cut away the rind from the bacon and chop finely, frying in the butter while you peel and slice the shallot. Add the shallot to the bacon in the pan and sauté together for a few minutes. Wipe the tomatoes, chop them roughly, then add to the pan mixture. Lower the heat, cover the pan, and cook gently for 5–7 minutes. Reserve 2 tablespoons of stock, and stir the rest into the pan. Blend the flour with the reserved cold stock, then add to the pan. Bring slowly to the boil, stirring continuously until the flour has thickened smoothly. Lower the heat, season to taste with salt and pepper and add the sugar, the garlic powder and a squeeze of lemon

For the tomato sauce
½ oz butter
1 small slice (rasher) bacon
1 shallot, or ½ small onion
½ lb ripe tomatoes
¼ pint chicken stock
1 scant level tablespoon flour
½ teaspoon garlic powder
½ teaspoon sugar
lemon juice

juice. Cover and simmer very gently for half an hour. Rub through the fine sieve of a food mill. Refrigerate.

Drop the canneloni into a pan of boiling water, to which you have added 1 teaspoon of salt and 1 tablespoon of oil. Bring to the boil, cover, and simmer for 15 minutes. Drain carefully and separate the pieces. Leave to cool. Meanwhile, prepare the stuffing. Melt the butter in a pan. Peel and finely chop the shallot or onion and add to the hot butter, sauté until tender, but not colored. Mince the meat and the garlic and add to the shallot in the pan. Season with salt and pepper, and stir in the flour and thyme. Remove from the heat. Add just enough stock to moisten the mixture so that it handles without crumbling. Divide the mixture into four portions, and with lightly floured hands shape into small rolls. Firmly roll up each one in a square of canneloni. Choose a small ovenproof dish into which the four rolls will fit neatly. Spoon a little of the sauce into the bottom of the dish, place the canneloni on top, spoon over a little more sauce and sprinkle with the grated Parmesan. Brown and heat through in a hot oven (400°F, 200°C or Gas No 6).

4 squares canneloni pasta
½ oz butter
1 shallot, or ½ small onion
4 oz cold cooked beef or lamb
1 small clove garlic
salt and freshly milled pepper
½ tablespoon flour
pinch of dried thyme
a little stock
1 tablespoon grated
Parmesan cheese

Galantine of Ham

Soak the ham in cold water overnight. Place in a pan and cover with fresh cold water, add the bouquet garni and bring to the boil. Cover and cook gently until tender for about 1 hour. Remove from the heat and allow to cool in the cooking liquid. Meanwhile prepare the aspic jelly.

Put 2 tablespoons of stock in a cup and sprinkle on the gelatine. Leave to soak for 5 minutes. Pour the rest of the stock into a saucepan, add the gelatine when it is spongy, and heat slowly. Whisk the wine, the egg white and the shell in a basin; tip into the pan of stock and whisk all together briskly until the mixture looks cloudy. Then stop whisking and raise the heat until the mixture starts to boil. Lower the heat and simmer in the uncovered pan for about 15 minutes, without stirring or disturbing the crust. Remove from the heat, pour the mixture through a double thickness of scalded muslin and leave to cool.

Remove the ham from the cooking liquid, and cut away the skin. Slice the meat thickly, then cut into small dice. Choose a small glass bowl of 1 pint or 1½ pint size and lightly press the diced ham into the bowl. Moisten with some of the cool jelly and leave to set. Add the chopped parsley to the remaining jelly and, when on the point of setting, pour carefully into the bowl. Chill in the refrigerator. An hour before serving loosen the edges of the galantine with a knife, dip the bowl in hot water, then turn out onto a serving dish and surround with watercress or shredded lettuce. Serve with the following salad.

1 lb cooked ham
bouquet garni
1 pint strong veal or chicken
stock
1 oz powdered gelatine
2 fl oz white wine
1 egg white and shell
1 tablespoon chopped parsley
watercress or shredded lettuce
(for garnish)

Bean and Mushroom Salad

Cook the beans according to the package, drain and allow to get quite cold. Wash the mushrooms, pat dry, then slice them thinly. Tip the beans and mushrooms into a bowl and stir in the finely chopped onion. Season with grated nutmeg and pepper and mix well with a good French dressing.

1 small package frozen broad or lima beans
3 oz button mushrooms
1 teaspoon finely chopped onion
a little grated nutmeg
freshly milled pepper
French dressing

Fresh Pears in a Custard Cream

Reserve 3 tablespoons of milk and heat the rest in a small saucepan until nearly boiling. Remove from the heat. Cream the egg yolks in a small basin with 1 tablespoon of the sugar. Sift the flour and cornflour together and add to the egg mixture. Blend in the reserved cold milk and, when smooth, add the hot milk from the pan. Stir well and return to the pan, bring slowly to the boil, stirring continuously, and cook for a few minutes. Remove from the heat and pour into a basin. Stir from time to time to prevent a skin forming as the mixture cools.

Meanwhile, whisk the egg white until it is stiff and then whisk in the remaining tablespoon of sugar. Fold this mixture into the cool custard. Lightly whip the cream and stir into the mixture until it is well blended.

Peel the pears thinly and slice evenly into a deep dish. Sprinkle with liqueur, if desired, and carefully pour the custard cream over the pears. Chill for several hours in the refrigerator. Before serving, sprinkle the top with toasted almonds.

$\frac{1}{2}$ pint milk
2 egg yolks
1 egg white
2 rounded tablespoons sugar
$\frac{1}{2}$ oz cornflour
$\frac{1}{2}$ oz flour
5 fl oz heavy (double) cream
3 fresh pears
1 tablespoon kirsch (optional)
1 level tablespoon flaked almonds, toasted

May

THE AFFLUENT LOVER

Russian Egg Mousse
Cold Salmon
Green Mayonnaise
Cucumber Salad
Pancakes with Cherries and Brandy

An evening in May calls for memorable pleasures, and this menu is not just full of expensive luxuries, but a beautiful balance of tastes and textures. The egg mousse, the salmon, the sauce and the cucumber salad may all be prepared in advance, but add the dressing to the latter not more than an hour before you need it. The luxurious pancakes, filled with plump, dark, brandy-flavored cherries, can be made ahead of time. Spread the pancakes out flat until cold, then stack them on a square of foil, fold it up into a loose parcel and store in the refrigerator or freezer. Allow to thaw on a plate at room temperature before filling with the cherries. A delicately flavored Rhine wine would suit this meal ideally and you should serve it nice and cold.

Russian Egg Mousse

Put the eggs in a saucepan of cold water and bring to the boil. Simmer for 8 minutes, then cool the eggs in running cold water. Remove the shells and leave in a basin of cold water until needed.

Sieve the egg yolks into a basin, finely chop the whites and add to the yolks. Measure 3 tablespoons of the stock into a small pan and sprinkle in the gelatine. Leave to soak for 5 minutes, then pour the remaining stock into the pan of soaked gelatine and stir over low heat until gelatine has dissolved. Remove from heat and allow to cool. You can stand the pan in a bowl of crushed ice to hasten the process. Lightly whip the cream. When the gelatine mixture starts to thicken, add it to the egg mixture and fold in the cream. Stir to blend evenly and season with the Worcestershire sauce and salt and pepper. Pour into a little china dish and spread level. Cover with foil, and chill.

When firmly set, turn the mousse out on to a plate and spoon the caviar over the top. Serve with hot toast or thinly sliced brown bread and butter.

3 eggs
$\frac{1}{4}$ pint veal or chicken stock
$\frac{1}{4}$ oz powdered gelatine
2 fl oz heavy (double) cream
$\frac{1}{2}$ teaspoon Worcestershire sauce
salt
freshly milled pepper
$\frac{1}{2}$ small jar caviar or Danish lumpfish roe

Cold Salmon

Leave the scales on, as they protect the skin and make it easier to remove. Generously butter a square of kitchen foil that is large enough to wrap loosely round the piece of salmon. Lay the fish on the buttered foil, season lightly and fold the edges of the foil together. Steam for 12–15 minutes, then leave to cool without unwrapping. When cold, remove the foil and carefully skin the salmon. Serve with green mayonnaise.

$\frac{1}{2}$ lb salmon
butter
salt and pepper

Green Mayonnaise

Previously prepare the mayonnaise. Wash the watercress, parsley and lettuce and remove the stalks where necessary. Put the greens in a small pan of lightly salted water, bring to the boil and cook for 5 minutes. Drain and rub through a sieve or fine food mill. Cool a little, then stir into the mayonnaise. If the sauce is very thick add $\frac{1}{2}$ tablespoon of boiling water. Lastly, stir in the cream. Serve cold in a sauce boat.

$\frac{1}{4}$ pint mayonnaise
small bunch of watercress
small bunch of parsley
2 or 3 lettuce leaves
salt
boiling water – see recipe
scant tablespoon cream

Cucumber Salad

Peel the cucumber, slice thinly and spread out on a plate. Sprinkle lightly with salt and put another plate on top, with a weight to press down. Leave for half an hour, then drain off all the liquid that has run from the cucumber and arrange the slices in a shallow dish. Put the sugar in a small jug or cup, stir in the vinegar until the sugar dissolves, then add the cream. Add the oil slowly and stir well to blend all the ingredients. Finish with a grinding of black pepper. Spoon the dressing over the cucumber and sprinkle with chives.

$\frac{1}{2}$ cucumber
salt – see recipe
1 teaspoon sugar
1 large teaspoon white
wine vinegar
2 tablespoons cream
1 tablespoon oil
freshly milled black pepper
1 tablespoon finely chopped
chives

Pancakes with Cherries and Brandy

First prepare the filling. Stone the cherries and sprinkle with sugar. Pour over the brandy and set aside while you prepare the pancakes.

Sift the flour and salt into a mixing basin and make a hollow in the center. Add the egg and half the milk. Stir the ingredients with a wooden spoon, gradually drawing in the flour from the sides of the bowl. Beat well until the batter is smooth and bubbles break the surface. Beat in the remaining milk and set aside. Just before using, stir in the oil. Pour into a large cup ready for use.

Melt the lard in a small saucepan and pour a little hot fat into the pancake pan. Heat until smoking hot, swirl the fat round the sides of the pan and pour back any surplus into the sauce-

For the filling
$\frac{1}{2}$ lb black cherries
1 tablespoon sugar
1 tablespoon brandy

For the pancakes
2 oz flour
pinch of salt
1 small egg
$\frac{1}{4}$ pint milk
$\frac{1}{2}$ tablespoon oil
a little lard for frying or a knob
of bacon fat

pan. Alternatively, rub all round the pancake pan with a knob
of bacon fat before pouring in the batter. Pour about 2 tablespoons of the batter into the center of the hot pan and tip it
about so that the batter runs over the surface to make a thin
pancake. Cook over a moderate heat to brown the underside,
then toss or turn and cook the second side. Repeat until all the
batter, which will make about six pancakes, is used. Stack the
pancakes neatly between two plates and set over a pan of
barely simmering water to keep hot. To serve, put a spoonful
of cherries on to each pancake, roll up and lay neatly along a
small ovenproof dish. Pour over any remaining brandy and
sugar and sprinkle with a little extra sugar. Keep in a warm
oven and pass under a hot broiler or grill for a few moments
before serving with chilled whipped cream.

THE IMPECUNIOUS LOVER

Lettuce Soup
Breast of Lamb with Apricots
Makke
Rhubarb with Lemon

The menu is spring-like and refreshing, but satisfying. The lettuce soup can be made beforehand and reheated; it is very delicate and smooth. The main course is a cold dish, using an inexpensive cut of breast of lamb, stuffed with a filling of apricots, onions and raisins. Serve it in thick slices with an unusual medieval dish of beans known as "makke." In those early days the potato had not reached Europe, so a floury or starchy vegetable made a good complement to other dishes. Makke has an attractive and tasty topping of fried onion, and is altogether nicer than mashed potato. The old recipe uses a little wine stirred into the bean purée, so if you are having a bottle of red wine with dinner, you can take a spoonful from it. Otherwise a spoonful of vinegar gives a little tang to a dish that your lover is not likely to have come across before. Lemon and rhubarb is a lovely combination of flavors, nice enough with or without the addition of cream. The whole menu is easily prepared in advance, with the lettuce soup and bean makke heated through before you eat. Flowers and candles are an unnecessary attribute; the scented spring dusk is romantic enough.

Lettuce Soup

Melt the butter in a saucepan. Peel and finely chop the onion. Add to the pan. Sauté gently for a few minutes until the onion is soft but not brown; peel and slice the potato and add to the pan. Stir the vegetables together and cook for a minute or two, then stir in the stock. Bring to the boil, cover, and simmer gently for about 15 minutes, until the potato is cooked.

Meanwhile wash the lettuce leaves and shred them coarsely. Add the lettuce to the pan, bring to the boil, cook for a minute or two, then draw off the heat. Put the soup through a fine sieve or food mill. Season with salt and pepper and return to the pan. Reheat when you are ready, and serve the soup with a sprinkling of chopped mint on each bowl if desired.

½ oz butter
1 small onion
1 medium potato
¾ pint chicken stock
1 small lettuce
salt
freshly milled pepper
a little chopped mint
(optional)

Breast of Lamb with Apricots

Trim away any surplus fat from the meat and lay skin-side down on a clean board.

Meanwhile prepare the apricot stuffing. Put the apricots and raisins into a saucepan, cover with cold water, bring to the boil and then drain. Cut the apricots into small pieces and put in a basin. Peel the onion, then cut into fine shreds and add to the apricots. Add the raisins, breadcrumbs and salt to the onion and apricots. Melt the butter and pour over all the ingredients in the basin. Mix together thoroughly. Spread the stuffing over the breast of lamb, to within ½ inch of the edges. Roll up and tie with string.

Melt the dripping in a saucepan and, when hot, brown the meat on all sides, then lift it from the pan. Peel and slice the onion, scrape and slice the carrot and tip into the pan. Place the meat on top and add enough water to cover the vegetables. Put the lid on the pan and bring slowly to the boil. Then lower the heat and cook gently for 1¼ hours.

Take the meat from the pan and leave overnight in a cool place. Before serving remove the string and serve in thick slices.

1 boned breast of lamb
small knob of dripping
1 onion
1 carrot

For the Apricot Stuffing
2 oz dried apricots
2 oz raisins
1 small onion
4 oz fresh white breadcrumbs
½ teaspoon salt
1 oz butter

Makke

Soak the beans overnight in cold water. Drain and put in a pan with plenty of cold salted water. Bring to the boil, cover and simmer for about 1 hour, or until the beans are soft. Drain well, and beat to a purée. Peel and chop the onion finely. Heat the oil in a small pan and gently sauté the onion until tender and brown. Warm the wine or vinegar and pour over the bean purée. Stir and season to taste. Scatter the browned onions on top and keep warm until ready to serve.

3 oz dried butter beans
or small lima beans
1 small onion
1 tablespoon oil
1 tablespoon red wine, or
vinegar
salt to taste

Rhubarb with Lemon

Trim and wash the rhubarb, and cut into 1-inch lengths. Put into a saucepan with the sugar, the strained lemon juice and thinly pared lemon peel. Bring slowly to the boil, then lower the heat, stir to dissolve the sugar and cook very gently for 5 minutes. Remove the pan from the heat and leave covered for a further 5 minutes until the rhubarb is quite soft, but not mushy. Take out the lemon peel and turn into a serving bowl. Cool and chill.

1 lb rhubarb
4 oz sugar
rind and juice of 1 small lemon

THE LOVER IN A HURRY

Pâté with Hot Toast
Trout with Almonds
Petit Pois (frozen)
Melon in Spiced Syrup

When you are pressed for time, this menu fits the bill, as very little preparation is needed. The first thing to make is the syrup for the melon dessert so that it has the maximum time to chill in the refrigerator. For the fish dish, you can sauté the almonds in advance and leave the trout, cleaned and rolled in flour, ready to sauté just before you dine. You will have ten busy minutes in which to reheat the butter in the pan, fry the trout on both sides, cook the petit pois, and dish them both. Have your oven warmed to 225°F, 110°C or Gas No 2, and pop the trout and peas in the oven while you enjoy your toast and pâté. The love of one's life might help with making the toast. Reward him or her with a bottle of dry white wine, dewy from the refrigerator, and lots of appreciative kisses.

Pâté with Hot Toast

Buy 4 oz of a good quality pâté – there are so many to choose from that you must be guided by your own preference. Serve in a thick slice on individual plates. Make the toast when you are ready to eat, so that it is fresh and hot. Unsalted butter seems to go best with pâté, but is not essential.

Trout with Almonds

Gut and wash the trout and pat dry. Snip off some of the fins and the tail, but leave the head on. Then roll each fish in a little seasoned flour. Heat the butter in a large frying pan and shake in the flaked almonds. Fry them until they are evenly golden-brown, then lift them on to a plate with a slotted spoon. Put the trout into the pan and fry for about 5 minutes on each side. Lift them on to a warm serving dish and cover with the browned almonds. Keep warm in the oven.

2 trout
seasoned flour
2 oz butter
1 oz flaked almonds

Serve with a dish of petit pois, the best of all frozen peas. Have ready a pan of hot water. Just before you start your meal, bring the water to the boil with a pinch of salt. Add the package of peas, reboil and cook for 3 minutes, drain, dish and top with a pat of butter. Put the peas in the warm oven with the trout until you have eaten your first course.

Melon in Spiced Syrup

Put the melon in the refrigerator; then prepare the syrup. Put the sugar and water into a small pan, stir over low heat until the sugar dissolves, then bring to the boil and boil fast for 3 minutes. Draw off the heat and stir in the sherry, cinnamon, ginger and lemon juice. Pour into a cold basin and put in the refrigerator until cool. Cut the melon into four, remove the seeds, then dice as much of the flesh as you need and stir into the cooled syrup. Spoon into two glasses and return to the refrigerator until required.

1 small melon
2 tablespoons sugar
2 tablespoons water
1 tablespoon dry sherry
$\frac{1}{2}$ teaspoon cinnamon
$\frac{1}{2}$ teaspoon ground ginger
1 tablespoon lemon juice

THE LOVER WITH TIME TO SPARE

Crab Mousse
Braised Lamb
Potatoes with Cheese
Braised Celery
Orange Cream

This menu comprises a grand dinner party on a small scale. No restaurant can provide better food than that cooked at home with loving care, and your lover should feel gratified to have secured a cook of such distinction. The beauty of the menu is that the first course and the last are best prepared the day before, and the main dish of braised meat and vegetables can be covered and kept absolutely safely in a warm oven. If the evening is warm and beautiful, a light rosé would be a delicious wine. Choose a few deep, dark red carnations, clove-scented and formal, to put on your table in a silver or pewter mug, with a little silvery foliage to soften the stiff lines of the flowers. You should both be filled with a sense of well-being, whatever the next day brings, after a dinner cooked with such unstinting care.

Crab Mousse

Make this dish the day before, and keep in a cool place. An hour before serving put into the refrigerator.

If using frozen shellfish, set the package to thaw at room temperature. If using uncooked shrimps, poach in a very small quantity of white wine for 10 minutes. Drain and cool. Wipe the tomatoes, chop them coarsely and put in a saucepan. Slice the pimento and add to the pan. Peel and finely slice the onion and peel and crush the garlic and add these to the pan with a seasoning of salt and pepper, the bouquet garni, and the lemon peel. Cover the pan and set over a low heat to stew for about 20 minutes, stirring occasionally to pulp the mixture. When soft, remove the bouquet garni and the lemon peel and put through a fine sieve or food mill. Set aside to cool.

Put the powdered gelatine and the cold water in a small pan. Leave to soak for 5 minutes, then set over a low heat until the gelatine has dissolved and the liquid is clear. While it is still

4 oz crab meat or shrimps
(may be frozen)
1 lb ripe tomatoes
1 canned pimento
½ small onion
small clove garlic
salt
freshly milled pepper
bouquet garni
a few shreds of lemon peel
½ level tablespoon powdered
gelatine
2 tablespoons water
2 fl oz mayonnaise
2 fl oz cream
a few lettuce leaves

warm, stir the dissolved gelatine into the tomato purée. Stir the mayonnaise into this mixture and allow to get quite cold. Lightly whip the cream and fold into the mixture. When it is on the point of setting, pour a little into the bottom of an oiled mold. Add a layer of well-drained shellfish, then finish with a layer of the tomato-flavored mixture. Leave to set. Just before serving, turn out of the mold on to a dish of shredded lettuce leaves.

Braised Lamb

Trim the meat and cut into small, thick slices. Heat the butter in a large pan and brown the pieces of lamb on all sides. Lift the meat out on to a plate. Scrape the carrot, peel the onion and scrape the celery. Chop all the vegetables finely and tip them into the pan, adding a little more butter if needed. Cover the pan and set over a low heat for 5 minutes until the vegetables have begun to soften, then put the pieces of lamb on top of the vegetables, add the wine and stock and a little salt and pepper. Cover the pan and cook very gently over a low heat for $1-1\frac{1}{4}$ hours. Lift the meat on to a warm serving dish, put the vegetables and gravy through a sieve or food mill, then pour into a saucepan. Adjust the seasoning and bring to the boil. If the gravy needs thickening, reduce it a little by boiling in the uncovered pan. Pour it over the lamb and keep warm.

1 lb lean lamb, cut from the leg
1 oz butter
1 carrot
1 onion
1 stick celery
2 tablespoons white wine
$\frac{1}{4}$ pint strong stock
salt
freshly milled pepper

Potatoes with Cheese

Peel and slice the potatoes thinly and generously butter a fireproof dish. Crush the garlic and grate the cheese. Arrange the potato slices in layers with a good seasoning of salt and pepper and the garlic and grated cheese between the layers. Top with a layer of cheese. Pour the stock into the dish and bake in a hot oven (375°F, 190°C or Gas No 5) for about 45 minutes, until the potatoes are tender and browned on top.

2 large potatoes (about $\frac{3}{4}$ lb)
1 oz butter
salt
freshly milled pepper
1 clove garlic
2 oz Gruyère cheese
$\frac{1}{4}$ pint stock

Braised Celery

Trim the celery and wash enough of the good stems for a dish. Cut the stems across to half their length. Peel the onion, scrape the carrot and chop them both. Heat the butter in a fireproof dish which has a lid. Tip in all the vegetables, cover and let them sweat in the butter for 5 minutes. Then pour in the stock and season with salt and pepper. Cover with a well-fitting lid, or add an inner lid of foil, and cook in the oven (375°F, 190°C

1 small head celery
1 small onion
1 small carrot
$\frac{1}{2}$ oz butter
$\frac{1}{4}$ pint jellied stock, preferably made from natural meat juices

or Gas No 5) for about an hour. Baste once or twice during the cooking time. When the celery is tender, lift it from the oven dish on to a clean heatproof dish, strain the cooking liquid over the celery to remove the pieces of carrot and onion. Keep warm.

Orange Cream

Rub each lump of sugar over the skin of the orange to absorb the oils, then place the lumps in a small pan with the milk over a low heat. Put the egg yolks and sugar into a small basin and beat together with a wooden spoon until thick and light. Pour the warm milk into this mixture, then return to the pan and stir continuously over a moderate heat until the mixture thickens but does not boil. Remove from the heat and strain into a basin. Set aside until cool. Soak the gelatine and orange juice in a small pan for 5 minutes; then heat gently until the gelatine dissolves and the liquid is clear. Stir the dissolved gelatine into the custard mixture and stand the basin in a bowl of ice, stirring occasionally while the mixture thickens. Lightly whip the cream and stir 2 tablespoons into the custard, reserving the rest for decoration. Pour the custard mixture into a small soufflé dish and leave to set. Sprinkle the top with a little grated chocolate and use the remaining cream to pipe a border round the edge of the dish.

3 lumps sugar
1 small orange
½ pint milk
2 egg yolks
1 level tablespoon sugar
1 level teaspoon powdered gelatine
1 tablespoon orange juice
5 fl oz heavy (double) cream
a little grated chocolate

The first green gooseberries of the season are so good that I have given the following soufflé as an alternative to the Orange Cream should there be new gooseberries in the shops. If you have an elder tree, two or three clusters of elder flowers tied up in muslin and stewed with the gooseberries adds a wonderful muscat grape flavor.

Gooseberry Soufflé

Top and tail the gooseberries and stew them very slowly with 1 tablespoon water until they are soft. If you have used the elder flowers, remove them, then rub the gooseberries through a sieve or Mouli food mill. Allow to cool.

Put the gelatine and water into a small pan and leave to soak for 5 minutes. Separate the egg yolks and whites into two separate basins. Add the sugar and gooseberry purée to the yolks and stand this basin over a pan of hot water, whisk until the mixture is thick, then remove from the heat. Stand the basin on a damp cloth and continue to whisk for 5 minutes.

1 lb gooseberries
1 tablespoon water
2 eggs
3 tablespoons sugar
¼ oz gelatine (half of ½ oz package)
3 tablespoons water
1 or 2 drops green coloring
2½ fluid oz cream

Taste to see if the gooseberries are sweet enough, and, if not, add a little more sugar.

Put the pan of gelatine over a low heat until the liquid is clear, but do not let it boil. Allow to cool slightly, then whisk into the gooseberry mixture. Stir one or two drops of green coloring into the mixture and leave in a cool place until on the point of setting.

Lightly whip the cream and fold into the thickened gooseberry mixture, then beat the egg whites until stiff and quickly fold them into the rest. Pour at once into a small soufflé dish and serve cold, but not chilled.

June

THE AFFLUENT LOVER

Caviar and Cream Dip
Cold Roast Duck with Rice Salad
Asparagus Vinaigrette
· Melone Ripieno

Perhaps the setting for this delectable dinner should be a terrace overlooking the Mediterranean! But wherever you are, all the dishes are relevant to a glorious evening in June, all are prepared in advance, thus leaving you free to savor each luxurious course as the evening slowly unwinds. Lovely, expensive champagne will add sparkle to the pleasures of two unashamed sybarites.

Caviar and Cream Dip

Turn out the caviar into a small basin. Whip the cream lightly and add about 4 tablespoons to the caviar. (Keep the rest to serve with coffee.) Peel the garlic and crush with a knife together with a pinch of salt; use about ¼ teaspoon of crushed garlic and stir into the cream and caviar mixture until all is well blended. Heap the caviar dip into a small bowl and chill. Serve either with fingers of hot, unbuttered toast, or hand a dish of potato crisps to dip and eat while you drink an apéritif.

1 tiny jar caviar, or ½ small pot
Danish lumpfish roe
5 fl oz heavy (double) cream
(see recipe)
½ clove garlic
salt

Cold Roast Duck with Rice Salad

Prick the skin of the duck all over with a fork, and rub some coarse salt into the breast. Put in a roasting pan with 3 tablespoons of cold water and roast in a moderate oven (350°F, 180°C or Gas No 4) for about 1 hour, allowing 15 minutes to the pound, and 15 minutes over, until the skin is brown and crisp and, when pierced, the thigh is not pink inside. Lift from the roasting pan and set aside.

   Meanwhile wash the giblets and put them in a pan of cold, salted water. Boil up and cook gently for 45 minutes. Strain the stock into a basin and reserve about ½ pint for the rice.

1 young duckling, about 3 lb
salt
3 tablespoons cold water

Rice Salad

Peel and finely chop the onion, remove the seeds from the pepper and shred the flesh finely. Melt the butter in a small pan and add the onion and green pepper. Cook over a low heat in the covered pan until the onion is soft, but not colored. Add the raisins and cook for a minute or two. Shake in the rice and stir well with a wooden spoon, then add the stock and a good pinch of salt; bring to the boil, cover with a lid, and cook gently over a low heat until the rice is tender and the liquid absorbed – about 15–20 minutes. Tip the rice into a large strainer and allow to cool. Before serving, lightly stir the cooked peas into the rice.

To serve, carve the best portions from the duck, and arrange on a dish with a surrounding of rice salad.

1 small onion
½ green pepper
½ oz butter
1 tablespoon seedless raisins
4 oz long-grain rice
½ pint giblet stock
salt
small cup cooked peas

Asparagus Vinaigrette

Cut off the tough ends from the asparagus and scrape away the outer skin and scales below the green part of each stalk. Wash in a large bowl of cold water, then tie into a bundle with string or tape. Have ready a large saucepan of boiling, salted water and lower the asparagus bundle into it. Bring again to the boil, then lower the heat and cook gently for 15 minutes. Lift the asparagus on to a dish or folded tea towel. Snip the string and leave to drain until cold.

1 small bundle asparagus, allow 8–10 spears for each portion

Sauce Vinaigrette

Put all the ingredients except the tomato and egg into a screw-topped jar and shake together vigorously. Peel the tomato by scalding in boiling water, discard the seeds and chop the flesh finely. Chop about half the white of the hard-boiled egg very finely. Stir these into the oil and vinegar mixture. To serve, spoon some of the sauce over each helping of asparagus.

1 teaspoon finely chopped onion
½ teaspoon finely chopped capers
salt and freshly milled pepper
½ teaspoon French mustard
½ tablespoon chopped parsley
1 tablespoon wine vinegar
3 tablespoons olive oil
1 tomato
1 hard-boiled egg (white only)

Melone Ripieno

Slice the top off the melon and scoop out the seeds. Then scoop out the flesh with a spoon and put it into a basin. Hull and halve the strawberries and add them with the raspberries to the melon. Set aside to chill. Put the sugar and water in a small pan, bring to the boil, stirring continuously, and boil for 2 minutes. Remove from the heat and stir in the Maraschino. When the syrup is cool, peel and slice the banana, but use only half if it is large. Add the banana slices to the other fruit and pour over the syrup. Chill thoroughly and then spoon the fruit and syrup into the hollow melon and keep chilled until needed.

1 small melon
About 2 oz each strawberries, raspberries and sliced banana
1 level tablespoon sugar
2 tablespoons water
1 tablespoon Maraschino

THE IMPECUNIOUS LOVER

Tomato Mousse
Caribbean Chicken
Broad Beans
Gooseberry Fool

All the dishes are suited to a lovely summer evening. The tomato mousse is a cool and refreshing starter, and the chicken dish full of piquant flavors. Nothing is nicer than a dish of young broad beans, but the sharp-sweet chicken with rice is quite enough on its own, if vegetables are expensive. A cool, pale gooseberry fool is a marvelous summer dessert; gooseberries have an all-too-short season, so make them a must in June. An inexpensive bottle of white wine, or lager beer, would be excellent served cold from the refrigerator. If you can find a few sweetly scented, old-fashioned roses for the table, arrange them in a cup; they will poetically suggest your adoring thoughts.

Tomato Mousse

Turn out the can of tomatoes into a small pan. Add a seasoning of salt and pepper and the sugar. Crush the garlic and add to the pan of tomatoes, then bring slowly to the boil, stirring thoroughly. Simmer for 5 minutes. Meanwhile soak the gelatine and water in a small cup for 5 minutes, then stir into the pan of hot tomato. Remove from the heat and pass the contents of the pan through a strainer or fine sieve, add a squeeze of lemon juice and adjust the seasoning. You should have about $\frac{1}{2}$ pint of purée. Divide this between two glass or china bowls, and leave to set in the refrigerator. Sprinkle each bowl with chopped basil or parsley, and serve with crispbread, or wholemeal bread and butter.

1 small can tomatoes
salt and freshly milled pepper
1 level teaspoon sugar
small clove garlic
$\frac{1}{2}$ tablespoon powdered gelatine
2 tablespoons water
squeeze of lemon juice
2 teaspoons chopped basil or parsley

Caribbean Chicken

Roll the chicken joints in seasoned flour. If using frozen chicken, first thaw at room temperature for several hours and drain well. Melt the butter in a pan and add the chicken joints. Fry on all sides until golden brown. Lift out the chicken into a small ovenproof dish with a lid. Peel and slice the onion finely, and skin and slice the tomato; add them to the butter in the pan, and sauté until the onion is soft and yellow, then spoon the mixture into the chicken dish. Drain the syrup from the can of pineapple into a measuring jug and add enough water to make up to just over ¼ pint. Pour into a small saucepan with the sugar, vinegar and chutney. Bring slowly to the boil, stirring continuously, then simmer for 3 minutes. Remove from the heat and pour the mixture over the chicken. Put the lid on the dish and cook in a moderate oven (350°F, 180°C or Gas No 4) for 45 minutes. Cut the pineapple into small pieces and add to the chicken dish, with a squeeze of lemon juice, about 10 minutes before the end of the cooking time.

Serve on a bed of plain boiled rice and keep warm in a slow oven until needed.

If you feel like a vegetable dish, a dish of young broad beans (lima beans) would be good. Pod the beans not more than a couple of hours before you cook them. Have ready a pan of boiling salted water, drop the beans in the pan, bring back to the boil and cook for 7–10 minutes, while you are eating the first course. Drain and serve.

2 large chicken joints
seasoned flour
1 oz butter or margarine
1 small onion
1 tomato
1 small (½ lb) can pineapple
1 tablespoon brown sugar
1 tablespoon malt vinegar
1 tablespoon sweet chutney
squeeze of lemon juice (optional)

Gooseberry Fool

Top and tail the gooseberries. Wash and drain them and put them in a pan with the water. Bring slowly to the boil, cover and simmer very gently for about 10 minutes until the fruit is soft. Remove from the heat and rub through a fine sieve or food mill. Leave to cool. When cold, add enough sugar to the purée to taste pleasantly sweet. Make up a small amount of custard. When cool strain the custard into the gooseberry purée.

Lightly whip the cream and stir two heaped tablespoons into the gooseberry mixture, reserving the rest of the cream to serve with your coffee. Turn the fool into a glass or china dish and chill. Sponge fingers or little sweet biscuits are delicious to nibble with the gooseberries.

1 lb gooseberries
1 tablespoon water
sugar – see recipe
5 fl oz heavy (double) cream – see recipe
sponge fingers or sweet biscuits

For custard
¼ pint milk
2 level teaspoons custard powder
1 teaspoon sugar

THE LOVER IN A HURRY

Globe Artichokes with Melted Butter
Salad Niçoise
French Bread
Strawberries and Cream

Although the artichokes sound slow to prepare, their largest requirement is that they be soaked in cold water to wash out any grit, so start your preparations by trimming them and setting them to soak, and then get on with making the salad. The vegetables may be varied according to what you have in hand, or can buy; the important thing to aim for is a good mixture, a good dressing and an attractive arrangement. If tuna fish is unobtainable, shredded ham, chicken, or shrimps are equally good. This easily put-together meal is a little gourmet dinner, appetizing and light for an evening of high summer. Who can resist strawberries and cream? Why bother with making a dessert when they are in season? They have the sweetness and sharpness of love itself!

Globe Artichokes with Melted Butter

Trim the artichoke stalks level with the base, remove any tough or discolored leaves, and snip off the pointed tops of the leaves. Soak them in a bowl of cold salted water while you prepare everything else. Have ready a pan of boiling salted water with a dash of vinegar. Plunge in the artichokes, bring back to the boil and simmer for $\frac{1}{2}$ an hour. Drain upside down, then keep warm. Serve with plenty of melted butter.

2 globe artichokes
4 oz butter

Salad Niçoise

Wash and drain the lettuce leaves. Cook the beans or peas according to the instructions on the package, drain and leave to cool. Peel and slice the cucumber, scald the tomatoes, remove the skins and seeds, cut them into slices. Peel the onion, slice finely and separate into rings. Arrange all the vegetables in a shallow dish and scatter the olives over the top.

Break the tuna fish and pile into the center of the salad. Spoon over the French dressing. You may add quartered hard boiled eggs, and strips of anchovy fillets, according to the time available. Serve with a crusty French loaf and butter.

a few crisp lettuce leaves
small package frozen beans or peas
$\frac{1}{2}$ cucumber
2 tomatoes
$\frac{1}{2}$ onion
6 black olives
6 oz tuna fish
French dressing

Strawberries and Cream

Hull the strawberries and put them in a pretty dish with a light sprinkling of sugar. Whip the cream and hand separately, with extra sugar.

1 lb strawberries
sugar
5 fl oz heavy (double) cream

THE LOVER WITH TIME TO SPARE

Gazpacho
Boned Stuffed Chicken
Green Salad
New Potatoes
Strawberry Sorbet

You will find that boning the chicken is not the terrible task it would seem, if you have a short sharp knife and set about the job slowly and patiently. Your care is well rewarded with the succulent layers of stuffed chicken breast, so easy to carve and to eat. The Gazpacho, one of Spain's famous soups, tasting deliciously of fresh vegetables, makes a wonderful start to the evening. And to round off a memorable meal, a light refreshing, slightly granular sorbet of strawberries is irresistible.

The whole menu may be prepared on the previous day, except for the salad and the new potatoes. You can make your preparations in an unhurried atmosphere if you give yourself a free afternoon in the kitchen and do your shopping in the morning. An evening in June calls for cool colors, airy rooms and a clear, fruity-tasting Rhine wine.

Gazpacho

Trim and chop the scallions (spring onions) and peel and dice the cucumber. Remove the seeds from the green pepper and cut into fine strips. Peel and crush a clove of garlic and reserve a small ½ teaspoonful. Scald the tomatoes and skin them, cut into quarters and discard the seeds. Cut any crust from the bread and soak in a little cold water, then squeeze it fairly dry. Put all these ingredients into a basin and add the oil. Then blend to a purée in an electric blender, blending small quantities at a time for the blender goblet to accommodate. Pour the purée into a basin and stir in the strained cold stock. Season to taste with salt, pepper and sugar, remembering that chilling will reduce the flavor, and, lastly, stir in the vinegar. Chill thoroughly and serve in two bowls with a sprinkling of sieved egg yolk floating on each.
Note: Any vegetables left over from the quantities given for soup may be added to the green salad.

2 scallions or spring onions
¼ small cucumber
½ green pepper
½ teaspoon crushed garlic
½ lb ripe tomatoes
1 thick finger white bread
1 tablespoon olive oil
¼ pint chicken stock
salt and freshly milled pepper
sugar to taste
½ tablespoon wine vinegar
yolk of 1 hard-boiled egg for garnish

Boned Stuffed Chicken

Before boning the chicken, prepare the stuffing. Trim any skin and fat from the veal and pork and put them through the grinder twice. Skin the ham and cut away the fat, then cut the fat into narrow strips and set aside. Mince or grind the remaining ham twice. Put all the ground meats into a basin with the breadcrumbs, the lightly beaten egg, the lemon juice and grated rind, and the seasonings, and mix together very thoroughly.

To bone the chicken use a sharp knife with a short blade. Put the bird on its side and slit down the back, and cut off the parson's nose. Work the flesh away from the back toward the leg joint as far as the thigh bone and scrape the meat away from it, then cut through the cartilage of the joint at each end. Remove the thigh bone, but leave the drumstick. Work the knife toward the wing, and cut through the cartilage where the wing joint joins the body, but leave the bone in. Work the knife under the breast to the ridge of the breast bone, then turn on the other side and start at the center back, repeating the process until you reach the ridge of the breast bone. Then cut very carefully along the ridge to free the carcass. Sprinkle the breast with a little lemon juice to keep the flesh white.

Place the boned bird on a board and pack in half the stuffing. Place the reserved strips of bacon fat over the stuffing, then add the rest of the stuffing. Fold the sides up and over the stuffing and press into shape. Thread a large needle with twine and secure the openings with stitches that you can snip and pull out after cooking. Fold the neck skin under the back, and secure with a stitch or two. Tuck the wings under the back and secure with a small skewer. Turn the bird on its back and press the breast into a nice plump shape and cover with the bacon strips or rashers. Take a piece of string and tie the ends of the two drumstick bones together, cross the string over the back, pass it round the wings and tie over the breast.

Scrape the carrot and cut in slices; peel and slice the onion. Spread the butter over a roasting pan and arrange the sliced vegetables on top. Place the boned chicken on the bed of vegetables. Put a square of buttered paper on the breast and cover completely with a large sheet of foil. Roast in a hot oven (400°F, 200°C or Gas No 6) for 20 minutes, then lower the heat to (350°F, 180°C or Gas No 4) and continue cooking for a further 1 hour. Remove the buttered paper and baste the bird 20 minutes before the end of the cooking time. Lift carefully on to a board and, when cool enough to handle, snip and pull away all the twine and string. Lift onto a serving dish and allow to get quite cold, before carving across the breast in thick slices.

1 small chicken, about 3 lb
a little lemon juice
4 strips (rashers) streaky
bacon
1 carrot
1 small onion
1 oz butter

For the stuffing
$\frac{1}{2}$ lb lean veal
$\frac{1}{2}$ lb lean pork
2 oz thick slice ham
2 oz fresh breadcrumbs
1 egg
1 tablespoon lemon juice
grated rind of $\frac{1}{2}$ lemon
pinch ground tarragon
pinch ground mace
freshly milled pepper

Serve with a green salad of crisp lettuce. Add the other half of the green pepper left from the soup, cut the flesh into strips, blanch in boiling water and refresh in cold. Add the remaining cucumber, peeled and sliced thinly, with perhaps a few radishes cut into flowers and two or three scallions or spring onions. Cook a dish of small new potatoes and serve them tossed in butter, with a sprinkling of chopped parsley.

Strawberry Sorbet

½ lb strawberries
1 tablespoon lemon juice
4 tablespoons water
small level teaspoon powdered gelatine
3 oz sugar

Blend the strawberries in a blender, then pour the purée into a bowl and stir in the lemon juice. Soak the gelatine in two tablespoons of water and put the rest of the water in a small pan with the sugar. Stir over a low heat until the sugar dissolves, then boil for 1 minute, remove from the heat and stir in the soaked gelatine. Allow to cool a little before stirring into the strawberry purée. When cold, spoon the mixture into a tub or carton and freeze for several hours until slushy. Turn into a chilled bowl and beat hard with a wooden spoon until smooth and light then return to the container, cover with a lid or foil and freeze until firm.

This is life, and nothing else is; life is delight; away, dull care! Brief are the years of man. Today wine is ours and the dance, and flowery wreaths, and women. Today let me live well; none knows what may be tomorrow.

The Greek Anthology

Supping in the bath can be tremendous fun.

Traditional hospitality requires that you offer your beloved the use of your bathroom before dining. Bathing, as such, can be a protracted business, and many have found that it pays to provide refreshment before the process is complete.

You can bathe in the garden . . .

. . . or in your bedroom.

Tho' poor in gear, we're rich in love.
Robert Burns

For the lovers who feel the need for privacy, the chambre separée *has always been there to provide it. In it you are served by a breed of blind waiters who appear to have been given eyes so that they do not see.*

The idea that love-making required privacy seems to have been confined to the 19th and early 20th centuries. Before then, people appear to have been quite uninhibited, flirting and making love outdoors as well as indoors, eating and drinking as they did so.

*I pursue love with gold; for bees do not work with
spade or plough, but with the fresh flowers of spring.
Gold, however, is the resourceful toiler that wins
Aphrodite's honey.*

The Greek Anthology

There is an oft-quoted saying attributed to Anon., that the loves of some people are but the result of good suppers, but love can still blossom and flourish on the simplest of fare, as poets have known since the day of Omar Khayyám and long before.

All other things, to their destruction draw,
Only our love hath no decay . . .

This, no tomorrow hath, nor yesterday,
Running it never runs from us away,
But truly keeps his first, last, everlasting day.
                    John Donne

You're so nice, I could eat you.

July

THE AFFLUENT LOVER

Iced Watercress Soup
Casserole of Beef Fillet with Wines and Brandy
Tossed Green Salad
Raspberries and Cream

The ingredients should be of the highest quality, so be selective and choose the finest. You will be rewarded by the exquisite flavors and textures in each dish and by the justifiable admiration of your partner. The chilled green soup should be silky smooth and peppery sharp with the taste of watercress. The casserole has a fragrance, when you lift the lid, that almost eclipses the melting tenderness of the wine-impregnated fillet, and to finish, the absolute simplicity of velvety raspberries and cream is in a class above more elaborate desserts.

So that affluence should not smack of opulence, place just one perfect, deep red rose beside your beloved's plate.

For your wine: Barolo, which the Italians consider the king of wines.

Iced Watercress Soup

Wash and chop the watercress, reserving two of the best sprigs. Peel and chop the shallot and peel and slice the potato. Melt the butter in a pan, add the shallot and potato and cook very gently for 5 minutes. Add the stock and milk and season with salt and pepper and the blade of mace. Cover the pan and simmer for 15 minutes. Add the watercress and simmer for a further 10 minutes. Remove the mace and put the soup through a fine sieve or food mill. Check the seasoning and chill overnight. Before serving, garnish each bowl of soup with a swirl of cream and the reserved sprigs of watercress.

1 large bunch watercress
1 large shallot
1 medium potato
¼ pint stock
½ pint milk
salt and pepper
blade of mace
2 tablespoons light (single) cream

Casserole of Beef Fillet with Wines and Brandy

Choose an oven-to-table metal casserole, with a well-fitting lid, into which the piece of beef fillet will fit snugly. Set the fillet aside. Pour the wine, Madeira and brandy into the casserole and heat very gently. Melt the butter in a frying pan. Peel and slice the onions and carrots and sauté them gently in butter until they soften and begin to brown. Then lift them out with a slotted spoon into the casserole of warming wines. Peel the tomatoes, chop them roughly, discarding the seeds, and add them to the casserole. Peel the garlic, crush half the clove, and add to the casserole with a seasoning of salt and black pepper. Cover the casserole tightly with foil and then the lid. Place in very slow oven (275°F, 140°C or Gas No 1) for 1 hour. Take out the casserole, and turn up the oven to (300°F, 150°C or Gas No 2). Reheat the butter in the frying pan, adding a little more if necessary and, when hot, brown the piece of fillet on both sides. Lift the meat onto the bed of vegetables in the casserole and cover as before with foil and the lid. Place in the bottom of the oven and cook for 30–35 minutes. Remove the foil and serve in the casserole with a dish of mousseline potatoes (see recipe in the Affluent Lover for January) and a tossed green salad.

1 lb beef fillet in one piece
1 wine-glass red wine
1 wine-glass Madeira or sherry
½ wine-glass brandy
1 oz butter
2 small onions
2 small carrots
2 tomatoes
1 small clove garlic
salt and freshly milled pepper

Raspberries and Cream

Shake the raspberries into a pretty glass bowl, pick over and throw out any that are not perfectly sound. Strew lightly with a little sugar. Turn the cream into a small basin, add a tablespoon of milk and whip together until soft and light. Spoon the whipped cream into a little bowl and hand separately with the raspberries and some extra sugar.

1 lb raspberries
sugar
¼ pint heavy (double) cream

THE IMPECUNIOUS LOVER

Mushroom Hors d'Oeuvre
Cold Roast Lamb with Garlic and Rosemary
Potato Salad with Green Peas
Fresh Strawberry Tarts

As the roast lamb and strawberry tarts are served cold, you can cook the meat and the pastry at the same time to utilize the oven. The menu is not nearly as extravagant as it sounds for someone on a tight budget. The hors d'oeuvre requires only ¼ lb mushrooms, and the delicious little strawberry tarts can be made with just a small punnet of fruit to decorate the tops of the creamy filled pastries. The piece of meat is the most expensive item, but the lean cut from the leg has absolutely no waste and, with the satisfying salad and two other courses, ¾ lb meat should be enough for two. The salad could be made with old potatoes and a small package of frozen peas, depending on the price of vegetables at the time. You can prepare the dishes well in advance; the hors d'oeuvre and the salad should be assembled last, but will still stand for an hour or more, leaving you time to set the scene for a delicious evening. Your meal will be worthy of the cleverest cook, and your lover should feel pampered and replete.

Mushroom Hors d'Oeuvre

Wash and dry the mushrooms and remove the stalks. Shell and finely chop the hard-boiled egg. Put all the other ingredients in a screw-topped jar and shake vigorously. Put the whole mushrooms and chopped egg into a shallow dish and pour over the dressing. Allow to stand for an hour or two before serving. Crisp bread rolls to mop up the dressing are nice served with the hors d'oeuvre.

4 oz button mushrooms
1 hard-boiled egg
½ tablespoon chopped parsley
½ tablespoon chopped capers
3 tablespoons oil
1 tablespoon vinegar
¼ teaspoon mustard powder
½ teaspoon sugar
salt and freshly milled pepper

Cold Roast Lamb with Garlic and Rosemary

Make several cuts in the meat with a pointed knife. Peel the garlic, cut into slivers and press a slip of garlic and a rosemary leaf into each cut. Rub the salt and pepper well into the meat and brush with a little of the cooking oil. Place the lamb in a roasting pan with the rest of the oil and cook in a moderate oven (350°F, 180°C or Gas No 4) for ¾–1 hour, basting occasionally until the meat is done. Allow to get quite cold. Cut the lamb across in thick slices and serve with mint sauce or mint, red currant or crab apple jelly.

¾–1 lb lean lamb, cut from the leg
2 cloves garlic
1 sprig fresh, or ½ teaspoon dried rosemary
salt and pepper
1 tablespoon corn oil

Potato Salad with Green Peas

Boil the potatoes in their skins for 15–20 minutes, according to size. When cooked, drain the potatoes, peel off the skins and cut into dice. Shell and cook the peas in boiling salted water for 10–15 minutes and, when tender, drain and cool. Peel and slice the onion finely and separate the rings. Put all the vegetables into a bowl, and season with salt and pepper. Spoon over the yogurt and mix gently together. A squeeze of lemon juice, or a small teaspoon vinegar, may be added to sharpen the flavor, or a little chopped mint may be sprinkled over the top.

1 lb new potatoes
1 lb green peas
½ small onion
salt and pepper
1 small carton yogurt

Fresh Strawberry Tarts (makes 6)

Line 6 greased small tart tins with pastry, prick and bake for 8–10 minutes in a moderate oven (375°F, 190°C or Gas No 5). Allow to cool before turning out.

Meanwhile, prepare the custard filling. Pour the milk into a saucepan and heat slowly until nearly boiling. Remove from the heat. Separate the egg and put the yolk into a basin with the sugar, whisk together with a fork, then sift the two flours into the sugar mixture and beat well with a wooden spoon. Stir the hot milk into the mixture. Then return to the saucepan and cook over a low heat for a few minutes, stirring continuously so the mixture thickens smoothly as it comes to the boil. Cook for a minute or two, then beat in the butter. Pour the custard into a basin and allow to cool, stirring occasionally to prevent a skin forming. When cool, whisk the egg white until it is stiff and fold about two-thirds of it into the custard. Fill the pastry cases with the mixture and arrange some whole, or sliced, strawberries on the top of each.

¼ lb pie or shortcrust pastry
¼ lb strawberries

For the custard
¼ pint milk
1 egg
1 tablespoon sugar
1 rounded teaspoon flour
1 rounded teaspoon cornflour
½ oz butter

THE LOVER IN A HURRY

Broiled (Grilled) Chicken
Fresh Tomato Sauce
Bread
Fresh Grapes and Cherries

If you wish to indulge in an eighteenth-century frolic and would like a slightly orgiastic meal, eaten with the fingers, it is easy to imitate the scenes of indulgence portrayed in *Tom Jones* and other historical movies. The quantities and varieties of meats traditionally consumed are obviously inappropriate for home catering, but bits of chicken or well-trimmed lamb chops are easy to cook in small quantities. Vegetables were probably not served with this sort of meal, so to make up for a lack of vitamin C a fresh tomato sauce in which to dip the chicken is very delicious. Large hunks of bread on which to wipe your hands – and to eat – would be in character. To follow, a bunch of grapes and some cherries lend themselves to flirtatious methods of eating.

Finger bowls are obviously vital, together with enormous napkins or small, smooth hand towels. If you do not have individual finger bowls, one large pretty bowl filled with water to which has been added a squeeze of lemon juice, a few tiny parings of lemon rind, some rose petals or one open rose will be both useful and decorative.

Coffee and liqueurs to be served in the bath?

Broiled (Grilled) Chicken

Wipe the chicken pieces and brush with the melted butter. Broil (grill) for 10–15 minutes on each side until cooked through.

Cut 4 large slices from the lemon and when ready to serve push a slice over the end of each protruding bone. This will act as a garnish and also a finger shield to stop the sauce running up your arm. Serve on small, hot plates with the bowl of sauce and a basket of bread.

2 chicken drumsticks
2 chicken thighs
1 tablespoon melted butter
1 large lemon
bread

Tomato Sauce

Melt the butter in a saucepan. Trim and chop the bacon; peel and slice the onion and carrot. Sauté the bacon for a few moments in the hot fat. Add the sliced onion and carrot and sauté gently for a further 5 minutes. Wash and quarter the tomatoes and add to the ingredients in the saucepan. Cover and allow to cook gently for about 5 minutes, or until the tomatoes are soft and the juices have been drawn out.

 Stir in the stock. Blend the flour with about 3 tablespoons of cold water, stir into the pan. Season with salt and pepper, then add the sugar and lemon juice. Cover with a lid and simmer for 30 minutes. Remove from the heat and rub the sauce through a sieve. Discard any skin and pips and reheat. Check the seasoning and serve hot in a bowl.

½ oz butter
1 small strip (rasher) bacon
½ small onion
½ small carrot
½ lb ripe tomatoes
¼ pint chicken stock
½ rounded tablespoon flour
salt and freshly milled pepper
½ teaspoon sugar
squeeze of lemon juice

Fresh Fruit

Wash the fruit, but leave the grapes in a bunch and use only those cherries which have their stalks still attached.

½ lb black grapes
or
½ lb ripe cherries
or both

THE LOVER WITH TIME TO SPARE

Zucchini (Courgettes) Vinaigrette
Shellfish Mayonnaise
Green Salad with Orange
Home-baked Poppyseed Rolls
Lemon Sorbet in Lemon Shells

This menu is ideally suited to a warm summer evening, full of refreshing flavors to sharpen the appetite and cooling ingredients to lighten any feeling of sultry heat. The lemon sorbet should be made on the previous day, and if you want to make the poppyseed rolls the day before, you can successfully reheat them by sprinkling them with a little water and wrapping them loosely in foil. Pop them into a hot oven for about 10 minutes, while you are eating your first course, and then unwrap and serve hot.

If you like a liqueur, some crème-de-menthe poured into two glasses containing crushed ice might be a delicious prelude to amorous adventure.

Zucchini (Courgettes) Vinaigrette

Trim zucchini or courgettes and place whole in a saucepan of boiling salted water. Simmer for 3 minutes, then drain and allow to cool. Peel the garlic and crush with a good pinch of salt. Slice the vegetables thickly and arrange in a shallow serving dish with the crushed garlic and a good grinding of black pepper. Place the remaining dry ingredients in a small saucepan, pour over the vinegar and bring to the boil. Boil gently, without a lid on the pan, for 5 minutes, then pour over the zucchini (courgettes) while still hot. Leave to cool and chill before serving.

½ lb zucchini (courgettes)
1 clove garlic
salt and freshly milled pepper
1 rounded teaspoon sugar
¼ teaspoon mustard powder
½ teaspoon dried marjoram
½ teaspoon ground coriander
¼ pint wine vinegar

Shellfish Mayonnaise

First prepare the cod or haddock by steaming on a plate over a pan of boiling water. Season with a little salt and pepper and cover with another plate. Steam for 10 minutes, until fish is cooked through, but remains firm. Take off the heat and, when cool enough to handle, remove any bones or skin and cut into cubes. Cut the shellfish meat up into neat pieces.

Peel the cucumber, cut into quarters lengthways and cut away the seeds, then slice into inch-long sticks. Add to a pan of

4 oz fresh haddock or cod
2 oz each shrimps, crab and lobster meat
½ small cucumber
6 stuffed green olives
¼ pint mayonnaise
½ teaspoon turmeric

boiling water, and reboil, then drain and cool. Mix the fish, shellfish and cucumber gently together, and arrange on a china dish with the olives spaced on top.

Mix the mayonnaise with the turmeric, salt and pepper and a squeeze of lemon juice. Stir together, then spoon over the dish of fish. If the weather is very warm, chill slightly before serving.

salt and pepper
squeeze of lemon juice

Green Salad with Oranges

Thoroughly wash and pick over the lettuce and watercress, discarding any outside or damaged leaves. Drain and pat dry in a clean tea towel. Using a sharp knife, cut away the outer skin and white pith from the orange, then cut out the sections of orange flesh, leaving the skin between the sections behind. Tear the lettuce leaves into easily managed pieces and break the watercress into sprigs. Mix together with about half of the orange segments in a chilled salad bowl. Before serving, pour over enough dressing to coat the leaves thoroughly.

1 lettuce
1 bunch watercress
1 orange
oil and vinegar dressing

Home-baked Poppyseed Rolls (makes 6)

Sift the flour and salt into a basin. Rub the butter into the flour with your fingertips. Warm the milk and water together until hand-hot, then stir in the sugar and sprinkle in the dried yeast. Leave in a warm place for about 10 minutes until spongy. Make a hollow in the center of the flour and stir the yeast mixture into this with a wooden spoon. When the mixture leaves the sides of the basin and forms a ball, turn on to a clean surface and knead into a smooth dough. Takes about 5 minutes. Shape into a ball and put in the basin, covered with a damp cloth. Keep in a warm place for about $\frac{3}{4}$ hour, or until the dough is double in bulk. Turn the dough onto a clean surface again and knead lightly. Divide into 6 equal pieces and shape into rolls. Space out on a greased baking tray and brush each roll with a little melted butter. Cover with a cloth and leave to prove for 10–15 minutes until puffy. Sprinkle each roll thickly with poppy seeds and bake in a hot oven (425°F, 220°C or Gas No 7) for 15–20 minutes. Serve warm, with curls of butter set in a dish with iced water and kept chilled until needed.

$\frac{1}{2}$ lb flour (plain)
$\frac{1}{2}$ teaspoon salt
$\frac{1}{2}$ oz butter
$\frac{1}{4}$ pint mixed milk and water
$\frac{1}{2}$ teaspoon sugar
1 level teaspoon dried yeast
melted butter, for brushing
poppy seeds

Lemon Sorbet in Lemon Shells

Halve the lemons and carefully squeeze out all the juice without damaging the peel. Strain and reserve the juice. Scoop out the remaining flesh from inside the lemons with a small spoon and pull away the thin white skin with the fingers. When quite clean, put 4 lemon halves in the freezer to chill.

4 lemons
4 oz sugar
$\frac{1}{2}$ pint water
1 egg white

Measure the sugar and water into a small pan and stir over a low heat until the sugar dissolves, then boil fast for 10 minutes. Leave to cool, then add the strained lemon juice, pour into an ice-cube tray and freeze for 2 hours, until the mixture is slushy. Turn the mixture into a chilled basin and beat smooth with a wooden spoon. Whisk the egg white until it is stiff and fold about half of it into the lemon mixture. Return to the ice-cube tray and freeze until firm. To serve, cut a slice from the bottom of each lemon cup so it stands firmly and fill with the sorbet.

August

THE AFFLUENT LOVER

Cold Fillet of Beef
French Rolls with Butter
Mixed Summer Salad
Melon

There are few things more conducive to passion and pleasure than the great outdoors, given sympathetic weather conditions. Whether you choose a hollow in the cliff tops from which to watch the setting sun cast a glow on the cheeks of your beloved, a sheltered woodland with the dapple of light and shade, or a fold in the hills where the cool air flows above you, you will look all the more beautiful and desirable to each other beneath God's heaven.

And the splendid thing about a picnic is that, however long you take for delightful encounters, the food will never spoil! And how good it will taste in the ensuing peace.

Cold Fillet of Beef

Beat out the fillets to about 1–1½ inches thick, brush them with oil and set them under a preheated broiler (grill) for 2 or 3 minutes until the outside is brown; then lower the heat for a further 3 or 4 minutes. Turn the fillets, brush the upper side again with olive oil, and put under the broiler (grill) at full heat for 2 or 3 minutes. Lower the heat and leave for another 3 or 4 minutes. If you don't like your steaks rare, give them 2 or 3 minutes longer each side when the heat is lowered. Grind a little black pepper over each steak, wrap loosely in foil and leave until cold.

Cut 2 crusty bread rolls in half, butter generously and sprinkle sparingly with salt. Put a crisp lettuce leaf, well washed and dried, on each half. Place the cold fillets on the bottom half of each roll, and close as a sandwich. Cut the rolls across into two for easier eating. Wrap the rolls tightly in foil, and leave in the refrigerator until you set off for your picnic.

2 round pieces of beef fillet,
3 or 4 oz each
olive oil
freshly milled black pepper
2 crusty bread rolls

Mixed Summer Salad

Separate the lettuce leaves and select only the pale green center leaves. Wash them very thoroughly and pat dry with a clean cloth. Drain the asparagus and artichoke hearts, if canned. Peel the avocado half, remove the stone and slice the flesh. Place all the salad vegetables and the olives in a bowl and mix well with the vinaigrette dressing until the salad is thoroughly coated. Turn into an air-tight container, and keep in the refrigerator until you are ready to leave.

1 crisp lettuce
1 small can asparagus tips
3 or 4 artichoke hearts, canned or freshly boiled
½ avocado
8 stuffed olives
vinaigrette dressing

Melon

Take the melon with you whole with sugar in a screw-top jar and a stainless knife with which to cut it in half.

The best small melon in season

Take plates and forks for the salad, and plates and spoons for the melon. Matching napkins and tablecloth on which to arrange your spread would be pretty and practical. A light, fruity wine, such as a Edesheimer Ordensgut would be delicious. If you fill a thermos with chipped ice and pack a plastic basin, you could stand the wine, and later the melon, in a basin of ice to keep chilled to perfection. If you are a die-hard for red wine with red meat, then choose a light claret, and forget about the ice.

THE IMPECUNIOUS LOVER

Pickled or Soused Herrings with Rice Salad
Brown Rolls and Butter
Fresh Plums
Coffee

Either buy pickled herrings or souse your own. See recipe below.

Soused Herrings

Split and clean the herrings, remove the heads and tails, and carefully remove the backbone. Roll up each fish from head to tail and pack side by side in a small ovenproof dish. Put the mace, peppercorns and bayleaf between the fish and sprinkle with salt. Peel and finely chop the onion and scatter over the herrings. Pour over enough vinegar and water to come about halfway up the fish. Cover the dish with foil, or a lid, and cook in a low oven (325°F, 170°C or Gas No 3) for about 1 hour. Allow to get cold.

2 fresh herrings
1 blade mace
4 peppercorns
1 bay leaf
½ teaspoon salt
½ small onion
equal quantities malt vinegar
and water – see recipe

Rice Salad

Scrape the carrot and grate it coarsely. Scald the tomatoes in boiling water and peel off the skins; chop the flesh and discard the seeds.

Put the rice and all the vegetables into a basin, stir gently and then add 3 or 4 tablespoons French dressing. Lift the herrings on to a plate and remove the skin and all the bones you possibly can. Break into pieces with a fork and stir carefully into the rice salad. Add a little more dressing if the ingredients are not well coated, but do not make the salad wet. Turn into an air-tight container, and refrigerate until you pack your picnic basket.

Butter the rolls, and take two plates and two forks for the fish salad.

Wash the plums and wrap in a paper napkin, or clean tea towel. Beer or cider would make delicious drinks, and a thermos of hot, black coffee never fails to round off a lovely evening.

2 cups cooked rice
1 small carrot
2 tomatoes
1 small package frozen peas, cooked
1 teaspoon finely chopped onion
French dressing

THE LOVER IN A HURRY

Salami and Bread and Butter
or Pizza
Bel Paese Cheese
Peaches

Make this an Italian meal. Nothing needs cooking, peeling, chopping or grating, but remember to take a knife and a corkscrew.

Line your basket with a pretty cloth. Wrap the pizza or salami, bread, butter and cheese in separate pieces of greaseproof paper. Top with a pair of luscious peaches and fold the cloth over them all. Tuck in a knife and a corkscrew and carry the Chianti by its raffia handle.

about 4 oz salami
bread
butter
or
2 wedges of pizza
$\frac{1}{4}$ lb Bel Paese cheese
2 ripe peaches
1 bottle Chianti

THE LOVER WITH TIME TO SPARE

Chicken Balls
Lettuce, Watercress and Orange Salad
Pineapple Dessert

Chicken Balls

Mince the chicken. Remove the crusts from the bread, soak it in a little milk and squeeze it dry. Put into a bowl the chicken, bread, egg, parsley, turmeric, salt and pepper. Knead thoroughly together and shape the mixture into marble-sized balls.

Roll the balls in flour and sauté them in deep oil until they are golden brown. Serve cold with lemon juice squeezed over them.

As well as the chicken balls take with you some tiny, cold, cooked new potatoes and, perhaps instead of the salad, some cold, cooked broad or lima beans. The flavors will combine excellently and all can easily be eaten in your fingers or with just a fork.

If the day should dawn pouring with rain, the dish can be eaten at home, hot.

2 cooked chicken portions, or
8 oz cold cooked chicken
2 large slices or 4 oz white
bread
milk (see recipe)
1 large egg
1 tablespoon chopped parsley
pinch of turmeric
salt
pepper
flour – see recipe
oil for frying
juice of ½ lemon

Lettuce, Watercress and Orange Salad

Wash the lettuce thoroughly and pat dry in a clean cloth. Select the best leaves. Wash and dry the watercress and tear off the coarse stalks. Carefully peel the orange with a sharp knife, removing all the pith and cutting the segments free of the membrane.

Put all the salad ingredients into a basin, pour over a few spoonfuls of dressing and mix thoroughly. Turn into an air-tight container and keep in the refrigerator until packing your picnic.

1 crisp lettuce
1 bunch watercress
1 orange
French dressing

Pineapple Dessert

Drain the pineapple juice into a small pan and soak the gelatine in the juice for 5 minutes. Then set over a very low heat until gelatine has dissolved and the liquid is clear. Measure into a small basin and make up to ½ pint with water, if necessary.

1 small can crushed pineapple
2 level teaspoons powdered
gelatine
5 fl oz heavy (double) cream

Cool and put in the refrigerator until beginning to thicken and set. Then fold in the crushed pineapple and the lightly whipped cream. Pour into individual dishes and chill until ready to pack. Wrap each dish carefully in foil.

Pack your picnic with care. The chicken balls can be eaten with your fingers, but you will need forks and plates for the salad. Spoons will be needed for the luscious pineapple dessert.

A bottle of sweet Sauterne or cans of lager beer would be equally good with this. A thermos of hot coffee with a dash of rum in it would wind up the picnic with a delicious treat as the sun goes down.

September

Chinese Dishes for Lovers

By KENNETH LO

Chinese cooking has many dishes designed for lovers. Whereas in ordinary cooking the majority of dishes are prepared by "quick stir-frying," most of the food for lovers consists of long-cooked, easily digestible dishes, often prepared with a generous amount of wine, and consumed in some bulk. We believe in a good feed before love.

The person cooking Chinese food for lovers must have three things on hand: *Gingsen Soup, High Broth* and *Superior Gravy*. With these, cooking of this type can be quite easy and simple and even prepared in a short time. But most dishes require time and care to produce.

The Gingsen Soup is prepared by slightly pounding 2–4 gingsen roots in a mortar and then placing them in an earthenware casserole. Add 1 pint of water and heat the casserole in a cool oven (275°F, 140°C or Gas No 1) for 2 hours, then reduce heat (250°F, 130°C or Gas ½) and place the casserole, tightly closed, on the floor of the oven to heat very slowly overnight. The resultant liquor is used for adding to soups and stews during the latter stages of their cooking.

The High Broth (about 2 pints) is prepared by simmering together 1 medium chicken, 1½ lb shin beef, 2 lb knuckle of pork (or spareribs after trimming away all fat), 1½ lb ham or bacon bone, in 4½ pints of water. Cut up the chicken into 2 wing joints and 2 legs, and chop the body into quarters. Cut the shin beef into 4–6 pieces, but leave the pork whole. Put all the ingredients into a large casserole and bring the contents to the boil, skimming away all fat and other extraneous matter. Place the casserole at the bottom of the oven (275°F, 140°C or Gas No 1) to simmer for a further 4 hours. First remove the chicken, beef, pork and bones, which can be used for other purposes, then skim once more for fat and impurities. In even more refined or elaborate cases, the broth is freshened just before using by adding ¼ lb of minced (ground) beefsteak, and ½ lb minced (ground) breast of chicken to the broth which is simmered for 5 minutes, and then carefully strained. The resultant broth of which there should be about 2 pints, should then be a very clear liquid, ready for use. It is often used for cooking briefly with meats, fish or seafoods which have previously cooked slowly in some other manner.

The Superior Gravy is prepared by placing 2 lb knuckle of pork, 2 lb belly pork, 1 lb leg of beef, and $\frac{1}{2}$ chicken in a large casserole with 3 pints of water. Joint and chop the half chicken into quarters and cut the beef and belly pork into 4 pieces. Leave the knuckle of pork whole. Bring all the ingredients to the boil, cook rapidly for 5 minutes, remove from the heat and pour away the water. Add $\frac{1}{2}$ pint of Chinese yellow wine (or dry sherry), 7 tablespoons of the best soya sauce, 2 teaspoons sugar, and 3 slices root-ginger. Turn the contents over several times, cover the casserole tightly and place at the bottom of a cool oven (275°F, 140°C or Gas No 1) for $3\frac{1}{2}$ hours. Add a further $\frac{1}{4}$ pint of water and $\frac{1}{4}$ pint dry sherry or yellow wine. Stir the contents round a few times and leave to cook for another 2 hours. Strain off all the solid contents (which can be used for other purposes or eaten as dishes in their own right) and leave the liquid at the bottom of the casserole to cool. Place in a refrigerator until a thick layer of fat which can be easily removed, has formed on top of the gravy. The liquid will form a jelly which is the Superior Gravy. It is frequently added to fish, seafoods and vegetables which require a short turn in a tasty sauce.

Note: Gingsen, Chinese wine and the other Chinese ingredients can be bought in any Chinese supermarket.

THE AFFLUENT LOVER

Shark's Fin Braised with Crab Meat
Quick-roast Fillet of Pork
Long-simmered Venison in Gingsen Soup
Steamed Eel in Pork and Black Bean Sauce
Braised Sea Cucumber (Bêche de Mer) with Seafoods

The following five dishes should be served singly, or at least not more than two at a time. They can be eaten with or without the complement of rice (if rice is served, it should be served in small Chinese wine-cup size bowls). Looking at the shape of the eel, sea cucumber and pork fillet, one is reminded of phallic strength, but it is the combination of Gingsen, wine, and the general richness of the foods which will work their purpose.

For two persons or two couples. Any leftovers can be appropriated for later use. At a Chinese dinner, foods are not meant to be totally consumed at one sitting.

Shark's Fin Braised with Crab Meat

Trim the fins with a sharp knife, cutting away irregular parts and edges, and soak them overnight in water. Pour away the water and place the fins in a pan of fresh, cold water. Bring gently to the boil and simmer for 2 hours. Pour away the water and add 2 pints of Secondary Broth; bring gently to the boil and simmer for a further 2 hours. Drain.

Heat 2 tablespoons of lard in a heavy casserole. Add half the wine, 2 slices of root-ginger, and 2 pints of Secondary Broth to the fins. Bring to the boil and simmer gently for 1 hour. Change the broth, repeat the process, and simmer for the same length of time. Drain the fins.

Now place the fins in an earthenware casserole. Add the Gingsen Soup, High Broth and sherry. Bring gently to the boil, stir in the cornflour mixture and simmer for 3 minutes. Adjust the seasoning. Ladle ¾ of the contents into a large china or porcelain serving bowl. Add 1 tablespoon of lard to the crab meat in the casserole. Bring gently to the boil and simmer for one more minute. Ladle out the contents and place on top of the fins and soup already in the serving bowl. Sprinkle with minced (ground) ham and serve. (Shark's fins are eaten mainly for their texture and orchestrated flavor. The mixture of crab-meat and minced (ground) ham gives color to the dish.)

3 lb dried shark's fin
6 oz crab meat
4 slices root-ginger
6 pints Secondary (i.e. bone) Broth
2 pints High Broth
½ pint Gingsen Soup
6–7 tablespoons white wine
3 tablespoons dry sherry
1½ tablespoons cornflour (blended in 3 tablespoons water)
salt (to taste)
3 tablespoons lard
2 tablespoons finely minced (ground) best ham

Quick-roast Fillet of Pork

Mix the ingredients for the marinade together until well blended. Turn and rub the fillet of pork with the marinade in a long deep-sided dish. Leave to marinate for 3 hours, turning the pieces of pork over every $\frac{1}{2}$ hour.

Place the pork on a wire rack to roast in a very hot oven (450°F, 230°C or Gas No 9) for 12–15 minutes. Put a pan at the bottom of the oven to catch the drippings. Turn the pork over once during the roasting.

Remove the pork from the oven and leave to cool for 20–30 minutes. When quite cool, cut with sharp knife into $\frac{1}{4}$ inch slices, arrange on a serving dish and serve with the other dishes.

2 strips of fillet of pork (approx. 2–2$\frac{1}{2}$ lb)

For the marinade
4 tablespoons soya sauce
2 tablespoons soya paste
1 tablespoon hoisin sauce
1 tablespoon honey
2 tablespoons dry sherry
1 teaspoon "five spices" powder (optional)

Long-simmered Venison in Gingsen Soup

Cut venison into 2 × 1$\frac{1}{2}$ inch pieces. Parboil in boiling water for 3 minutes and drain. Soak noodles in cold water for 5 minutes and drain. Cut scallions (spring onions) into coarse shavings. Crush peppercorns slightly in a mortar.

Place venison in a heavy casserole. Add ginger, salt, peppercorns and High Broth. Bring gently to the boil. Place an asbestos sheet under the casserole and simmer over a low heat for 1 hour. Add Gingsen Soup and simmer gently for another hour. Add yellow wine (or sherry) and noodles. Adjust for seasonings and simmer for a further $\frac{3}{4}$ hour.

Sprinkle with kaoliang (or brandy) and scallion or spring onion shavings. Serve in the casserole. As you can see, this is quite a winey dish.

2$\frac{1}{2}$ lb venison (or use mutton or goat meat)
4 slices root-ginger
2 teaspoons salt
1$\frac{1}{2}$ teaspoons peppercorns
$\frac{1}{2}$ pint High Broth
$\frac{1}{2}$ pint Gingsen Soup
$\frac{1}{2}$ pint yellow wine (or use dry sherry)
4 tablespoons Chinese kaoliang liqueur (or brandy)
2 stalks scallions (spring onions)
2 oz transparent pea-starch noodles

Steamed Eel in Pork and Black Bean Sauce

Cut eel into 2-inch sections. Shred pork into matchstick strips, chop ginger into coarse grains. Cut onion into thin slices, deseed and cut peppers into shreds. Soak black beans in water for 20 minutes, and drain. Rub eel with salt and ginger and leave to season for 1 hour.

Heat lard in a frying pan. When it has melted, add onion, peppers, pickles and pork. Stir-fry over high heat for 3 minutes. Add black beans and stir-fry for a further 2 minutes. Add Superior Gravy and sherry, and continue to stir-fry for 3 minutes.

Ladle one-third of the above mixture to spread at the bottom of a deep-sided, heatproof dish. Arrange the sections of eel on top, well spaced out. Use the balance of the mixture as a thick garnish to place on top of the eel. Place the dish in a steamer, and steam vigorously for 20 minutes.

Serve by bringing the heatproof dish to the table.

3 lb eel
2 teaspoons salt
4 slices root-ginger
2 tablespoons salted black beans
1 large onion
1 red, 1 green pepper
2 small chili peppers
3 tablespoons lard
4–5 oz lean and fat pork
4 tablespoons Superior Gravy
2–3 tablespoons Chinese snow pickles (or use shredded dill pickle or gherkins)
3 tablespoons dry sherry

Braised Sea Cucumber (Bêche de Mer) with Seafoods

Soak sea cucumber in 4 changes of water for 48 hours and drain. Place in a heavy pan with High Broth and slices of ginger and simmer gently for 2 hours. Drain and discard ginger.

Place sea cucumber in a heavy pot or pan. Add Superior Gravy, bring gently to the boil and simmer very gently for 45 minutes, turning over 2–3 times.

Meanwhile, heat lard in a frying pan. Add prawns or shrimps, clams, oysters and crab meat, and stir-fry them together for $1\frac{1}{2}$ minutes with the remaining ginger cut into fine shreds and soya sauce. Combine the cornflour and water and stir into the pan. Add the kaoliang or sake .

Add the seafoods to the sea cucumber and sauce and turn them over several times in a deep-sided heatproof dish. Place the dish and contents in a steamer and steam steadily for 30 minutes.

Serve by bringing the heatproof dish to the table.

1 lb sea cucumber (dry)
4 slices root-ginger
6 medium oysters
6 large prawns or 12 shrimps
6–8 clams
6 tablespoons crab meat
3 tablespoons lard
1 tablespoon soya sauce
$\frac{1}{2}$ pint High Broth
$\frac{1}{4}$ pint Superior Gravy
$\frac{3}{4}$ tablespoon cornflour blended in 4 tablespoons water
4 tablespoons Chinese kaoliang or Japanese sake

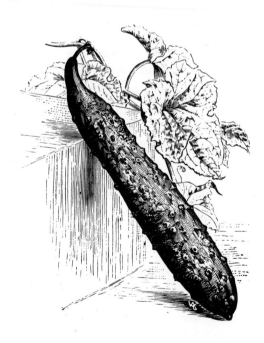

THE IMPECUNIOUS LOVER

Mixed Ingredient Congee
Soya Braised and Roasted Spareribs
Stir-fried Mixed Vegetables in Sweet and Sour Sauce
A Dish of Mixed Pickles

The problem here is to serve up a meal which is cooked from inexpensive ingredients and yet is as delicious as a more expensive meal. Being impecunious, one has more than ever to cater in some style: therefore the menu will feature four dishes, rather than just three, on which an average Chinese could just get by. When one is poor, one always starts with rice gruel or congee.

Mixed Ingredient Congee (rice gruel)

Chop chicken carcass into 4 pieces. Cut each Brussels sprout into quarters, discarding coarse outer leaves. Cut onions into quarters.

Rinse rice and place in a heavy casserole. Add water, sprouts, onion, dried shrimps and chicken pieces. Bring gently to the boil; place an asbestos sheet under the casserole and reduce to lowest heat. Simmer for 2 hours, turning the contents over once every 30 minutes. Add chicken stock cube, peas and salt. Simmer slowly for a further 15 minutes. Remove chicken pieces.

Serve in individual bowls, leaving the rest in the casserole for second helpings.

¼ lb rice
2 pints water
2–3 oz Brussels sprouts
1 tablespoon dried shrimps
1 medium onion
1 chicken stock cube
¼ chicken carcass
salt (to taste)
2 tablespoons green peas

Soya Braised and Roasted Spareribs

Cut pork into individual ribs. Cut onion into thin slices and shred ginger. Add onion, ginger, soya sauce, peppercorns, soya paste (or hoisin sauce), sugar, stock cube and water to the spareribs in a casserole.

Bring the contents in the casserole gently to the boil. Transfer them to a moderate oven (325°F, 170°C or Gas No 3) for 1 hour. Transfer the ribs to a roasting pan. Increase the oven temperature to 400°F, 200°C or Gas No 6) and return the pan to the oven for the ribs to crisp for 10 minutes. Add 6 tablespoons of water blended with 2 tablespoons of cornflour to the gravy in the casserole. Bring to the boil and stir round a few times. Pour this gravy into a sauceboat.

Serve the spareribs with gravy handed separately. You may pour the gravy over the ribs or add it, a little at a time, to the rice gruel you are eating.

1 lb pork spareribs
1 onion
2 slices root-ginger
2½ tablespoons soya sauce
1 tablespoon hoisin sauce (or soya paste)
2 teaspoons sugar
1 teaspoon peppercorns
½ chicken stock cube
¼ pint water
2 tablespoon cornflour (blended with 6 tablespoons water)

Stir-fried Mixed Vegetables in Sweet and Sour Sauce

Clean and cut carrot and zucchini or courgette diagonally into ½ inch slices. Break cauliflower into individual flowerets. Cut each tomato in quarters or sixes. Mix the sauce ingredients until well blended.

Heat oil in a saucepan. Add carrot, zucchini or courgette and cauliflower. Turn them in the oil over medium heat for 1 minute. Leave to cook for 2 minutes. Add the stock, bring to the boil and leave to cook over high heat until the liquid in the pan has been reduced to a quarter of its original amount. Add tomatoes and peas. Pour in the sauce mixture. Turn the contents over a few times. The sauce should thicken and become translucent within a minute. Leave to cook for ½ minute over gentle heat.

Serve in a deep-sided dish.

1 small head of cauliflower
2–3 medium tomatoes
3 tablespoons green peas
1 small zucchini (courgette)
1 medium carrot
2 tablespoons vegetable oil
¼ pint bone stock

For the sauce
1 tablespoon cornflour (blended in 5 tablespoons water)
1 tablespoon soya sauce
3 tablespoons orange juice
2 tablespoons vinegar
1½ tablespoons tomato purée
1½ tablespoons sugar
2 tablespoons red or white wine

A Dish of Mixed Pickles

It is traditional to serve pickles with congee whenever there is a shortage of savory food. Because of its watery content congees are usually fairly bland, though some are made rather savory. They are best consumed with small quantities of strong- or sharp-tasting items. Braised bamboo shoots, which are available in cans, can be served with the pickles. If there is a shortage of Chinese pickles, most western pickles (pickled beetroot, pickled capers, pickled red cabbage, pickled cauliflower or all pickles can be used instead. These only need to be served in a small plate or saucer, but they will help to add a distinctive item to the selection on the table.

THE LOVER IN A HURRY

Sub Gum Soup Noodles
Stir-fried Diced Chicken Breast with Shrimp or Prawns, Button Mushrooms,
Peas and Celery
Quick Stir-fry Spinach

The lover in a hurry may be much better off than the impecunious lover, but having less time to spare, he has to limit himself to just three dishes. Apart from the main dish, which in this case will be a noodle dish (a Chinese soup noodle is a main course which is often taken as a meal on its own), he has to fall back on two stir-fried dishes which seldom require much more than 5–6 minutes to prepare.

The two dishes, spinach and chicken and shrimps or prawns, which require no more than 10–12 minutes to prepare and cook, are quite different in color, and the flavors should act as excellent supporting dishes to eat with the main dish of noodles. Any lover should be flattered and impressed by being presented and served with three such flavorsome and delicious dishes in record time.

Sub Gum Soup Noodles

"Sub Gum" means "ten varieties," but in the present case we shall use no more than 5–6 ingredients to go with the noodles.

Add noodles to a pan of salted boiling water and simmer for 5–6 minutes, drain. Shred ham, chicken and cucumber. Cut scallions or spring onions into 1 inch sections; wash watercress and cut into 1 inch lengths.

Heat High Broth in a saucepan. When it starts to boil, add stock cube, half the ham and all the vegetables. After 10 seconds of boiling, add the noodles. Leave them to simmer together for 2 minutes, ladle them out and divide them into large bowls.

Garnish the two bowls of noodles with shredded ham and chicken. Sprinkle with sesame oil and serve.

$\frac{1}{4}$ lb or 3–4 "pads" egg noodles
1 pint High Broth
1 chicken stock cube
2 oz cooked ham
2 oz cooked chicken
1 cucumber (4 inch section)
$\frac{1}{2}$ bundle watercress
2 stalks scallions or spring onions
2 teaspoons sesame oil

Stir-fried Diced Chicken Breast with Shrimp or Prawns, Button Mushrooms, Peas and Celery

Shred ginger, clean and cut celery into $\frac{1}{2}$ inch lengths, cut chicken meat into $\frac{1}{4}$–$\frac{1}{2}$ inch cubes. Rub chicken and shrimps or prawns with salt, ginger and 1 tablespoon oil. Open can containing mushrooms and drain away the water.

Heat the remaining oil and butter in a large frying pan over a high heat. When butter has melted, add mushrooms, celery and peas. Stir-fry quickly for 1 minute. Add the shrimps or prawns and chicken. Stir-fry them together with the other ingredients for 1 minute. Sprinkle the contents with soya sauce, sugar and sherry. Continue to stir-fry over high heat for $1\frac{1}{2}$ more minutes.

Spoon onto a well-heated serving dish and eat at the same time as the soup noodle.

3–4 oz breast of chicken
2–3 oz shrimps or prawns
1 teaspoon salt
3 tablespoons oil
1 tablespoon butter
1 stick celery
3–4 tablespoons green peas
small can button mushrooms
2 slices root-ginger
1 tablespoon soya sauce
1 tablespoon dry sherry
$1\frac{1}{2}$ teaspoon sugar

Quick Stir-fry Spinach

Wash and dry spinach thoroughly. Remove and discard any tough stems and coarse discolored leaves. Chop garlic and onion finely.

Heat oil and lard in a large saucepan. When hot, add onion and garlic and stir-fry over medium heat for $\frac{3}{4}$ minute. Add the spinach and salt and turn quickly over high heat for $1\frac{1}{2}$ minutes, until all the leaves are glistening with oil. Add soya sauce, sugar and sesame oil. Lower to medium heat. Continue to turn and stir for $1\frac{1}{2}$ minutes.

Transfer the spinach mixture to a well-heated dish and serve.

$\frac{3}{4}$–1 lb spinach
2 stalks scallions or spring onions
3 cloves garlic
3 tablespoons vegetable oil
1 tablespoon lard
$1\frac{1}{2}$ teaspoons salt
$1\frac{1}{2}$ tablespoons soya sauce
1 teaspoon sugar
1 tablespoon sesame oil

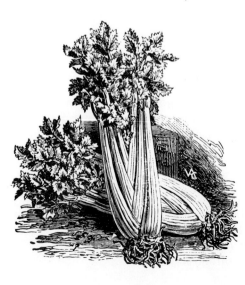

THE LOVER WITH TIME TO SPARE

Long-cooked Shin or Leg of Beef
Long-simmered Chicken with Chinese Cabbage and Watercress
Toasted Prawns or Shrimps with Sesame Seeds
Sliced Sole Poached in Oil and Braised with Green Beans
Paper-wrapped Chicken

Long-cooked Shin or Leg of Beef

Cut beef into 2 × 1 inch pieces. Place in a casserole and add water. Bring to the boil and cook for 4–5 minutes; skim away impurities. Crush peppercorns in a mortar, or with the side of a chopper and, with the salt and ginger, add to the beef in the casserole.

Place the casserole at the bottom of a cool oven (275°F, 140°C or Gas No 1) and leave overnight. Add red wine, Gingsen Soup and soya sauce. Stir and turn the contents over a few times. Raise the casserole to the middle of the oven and continue to cook at the same oven temperature for 4 hours more.

Serve by bringing the casserole to the table.

2½ lb shin or leg of beef
2 teaspoons salt
1 teaspoon peppercorns
4 slices root-ginger
1½ pints water
½ pint red wine
½ pint Gingsen Soup
3 tablespoons soya sauce

Long-simmered Chicken with Chinese Cabbage and Watercress

Clean chicken and place in a casserole with 2½ pints of boiling water. Cook for 6–7 minutes. Skim away impurities and pour off water. Add salt and root-ginger. Put an asbestos mat under the casserole and leave to simmer over gentle heat for 2 hours. Add wine, Gingsen Soup and stock cube. Cut the cabbage into 3-inch slices and insert under the chicken. Adjust the seasonings. Wash and pick over the watercress and lay on top of the chicken. Simmer for a further ½ hour.

Serve by bringing the casserole to the table.

1 medium chicken (3 lb)
2 teaspoons salt
2 slices root-ginger
1 chicken stock cube
1 small Chinese cabbage (or ¾ lb celery)
1 bunch watercress
¼ pint Gingsen Soup (optional)
¼ pint white wine
salt and pepper to taste

Toasted Prawns or Shrimps with Sesame Seeds

Chop shrimps or prawns and pork fat very finely. Add salt and pepper to taste, and the egg white. Mix and knead all together until thoroughly blended. Remove the crust from the bread. Beat the egg lightly and brush the bread with it on each side. Sprinkle one side of each bread slice with some sesame seeds, turn the slices over and spread a thick layer of prawn- (or shrimp-) pork mixture on top of each slice of bread (the mixture should be about the thickness of the bread itself). Sprinkle the top of the spread evenly with the remaining sesame seeds.

Heat oil until sizzling hot (test with a crumb). Lower 1 slice of bread at a time – prawn or shrimp side down – and fry in the oil for 3–3½ minutes (2 minutes prawn side down, and turn over for 1½ more minutes.) The frying can be done one piece of bread at a time, or 2 pieces at a time, depending upon the size of the deep-fryer.

Remove the bread from the pan and drain on absorbent paper. Cut each piece into 6–8 pieces (like small fish-fingers), and serve on a well-heated dish.

½ lb fresh prawns or shrimp meat
¼ lb pork fat
1 egg white
1 whole egg
salt and pepper (to taste)
4 slices bread
oil for deep frying
5–6 tablespoons sesame seeds

Sliced Sole Poached in Oil and Braised with French Beans

Cut fish into 2 × 1 inch pieces. Sprinkle and rub with salt and cornflour and brush with egg white. Top and tail the beans and cut into ½ inch pieces.

Heat half the lard in a frying pan (with lid). When hot, add the beans, stir the vegetables over medium heat for 2–3 minutes and sprinkle with salt and pepper. Add High Broth and Gingsen Soup. Turn the beans over, cover with lid and leave to simmer for 6–7 minutes over medium heat.

Heat oil in a deep-frying or other pan. When sizzling hot, remove from heat for ½ minute. Add the fish to the oil piece by piece and leave to poach very gently in the heat of the oil for 2½ minutes.

Transfer the beans from the frying pan to a heatproof dish and spread them out as a bed. With a perforated spoon, transfer the slices of fish from the deep-fryer and lay them on the "bed" of beans. Add the white wine and cornflour blended in a little water to the liquid in the frying pan, add the remaining lard, bring quickly to the boil and ladle them over the dish of sole and beans.

Serve in the heatproof dish. The contrast between the whiteness of the fish and the greenness of the beans makes the dish a very attractive one.

1 lb sole (filleted)
1 tablespoon cornflour
1 egg white
1½ teaspoons salt
oil for deep frying, about 1 pint
1 lb green beans
5 tablespoons High Broth
5 tablespoons Gingsen Soup
3 tablespoons white wine
2 teaspoons cornflour blended in a little water
2½ tablespoons lard
salt and pepper (to taste)

Paper-wrapped Chicken

Soak mushrooms in water for 30 minutes. Remove stems and cut caps into matchstick shreds. Cut chicken and celery into similar shreds, and scallions or spring onions into 1½ inch lengths. Cut ginger into fine shreds. Mix the ingredients for the marinade together until well blended. Add the shredded ginger and marinade to the chicken and leave to marinate for 30 minutes. Cut cellophane paper into 4 × 3 inch rectangular pieces. Divide the marinated chicken meat and the celery, scallions or spring onions and mushrooms into 12–15 equal portions. Place each portion lengthwise across the center of each rectangular piece of cellophane paper. Wrap the food materials firmly in the cellophane paper, envelope-fashion – by folding up the bottom edge over the stuffings, bringing in the two sides, and tucking in the last flap. Weigh down with an empty plate, as each envelope is made, so as to keep them firmly wrapped.

Heat oil for deep frying. When hot, lower in 2–3 "envelopes" of wrapped chicken to fry for 3 minutes. Remove and drain an absorbent paper and keep hot in a warm oven, while the other envelopes are being fried.

Transfer the "envelopes" from the absorbent paper to a well-heated dish, arrange nicely in a pile of delicious "messages."

¼–⅓ spring chicken
4 medium Chinese dried mushrooms
1 stick celery
2–3 stalks scallions or spring onions
2 slices root-ginger
oil for deep frying

For marinade
1½ tablespoons soya sauce
½ tablespoon hoisin sauce
½ tablespoon shrimp sauce (optional)
1 tablespoon dry sherry
1 teaspoon sugar
1 large sheet cellophane paper

When Cupid's wings are wet with wine
He cannot quit the fort he's taken.
                              Ovid

And when I thought how my friend my lover was on his way coming, O then I was happy,
O then each breath tasted sweeter, and all the day my food nourished me more, and the beautiful day pass'd well.
Walt Whitman

If only because one tends to get everything, even oneself, ready too soon, waiting is all too often the lover's lot, especially in China, where it used to be considered quite all right for a man to accept several invitations for the same evening and to go from one to another.

Thro' all the drama – whether damned or not –
Love gilds the scene, and women guide the plot.
                                        Sheridan

To enjoy food and rejoice in feminine beauty is only to be human.
Confucius

The day has broken, and for long early-rising chanticleer is crowing to summon envious dawn. A curse on thee, most jealous of fools, who drivest me from here to the tireless chatter of you men.

The Greek Anthology

To cheat a lover of an appointed night, and to cajole her by promises, is as bad as to have one's hands stained with blood.

Propertius

There is an importance of beauty which cannot be accounted for by there and then, and attacks me, but not separately from the welcome of the food, or the grace of her arms.

Bernard Spencer

There is a French saying that love and digestion went to bed together and the offspring was apoplexy. This isn't quite true.

The Joy of Sex

The feeling of friendship is like that of being comfortably filled with roast beef; love, like being enlivened with champagne.

Samuel Johnson

One cannot think well, love well, sleep well, if one has not dined well.
Virginia Woolf

Nothing can prepare the human mind for amiable intercourse better than a well-conceived and artistically prepared dinner.

Alexis Soyer

*Shower on us . . . the dewy rain of Bacchus; shower it
and refresh our picnic . . . and let our converse be of
love the bitter-sweet.*

The Greek Anthology

Shall I, after tea and cakes and ices,
Have the strength to force the moment to its crisis?
                              T. S. Eliot

October

THE AFFLUENT LOVER

Cantonese Lobster
Slow-cooked Steamed Duck with Mushrooms
Slow-simmered Sea Bass in Gingsen Soup
Quick-fried Sliced Steak in Oyster Sauce
Cherry Pork

In October, in most parts of China there is a slight nip in the night air and a certain chill in the touch of the sheets before the bodies have warmed the bed. October calls for dishes that are warm and caressing to go with one or two others which are spicy and somewhat stimulating. There is a good selection of such dishes in the repertoire of Chinese cuisine from which the affluent lover could choose.

Cantonese Lobster

Chop and crush garlic and shred and mince ginger. Cut scallions or spring onions into 1 inch segments.

Mix Broth or chicken stock in a bowl with sherry (or yellow wine), soya sauce, and sugar until well blended.

Beat eggs lightly in a cup or bowl. Prepare the lobster by chopping off the tail and cutting the body in half lengthways. Cut each half into 2–3 pieces. Crush the claws and joints to facilitate eating. Use shears to cut off the feelers, small claws and legs, and remove the sac near the eyes.

Heat oil in a large pan, or Chinese wok (frying pan with a round bottom). When very hot add the lobster pieces. Turn them in the oil for 1½ minutes and push to one side of the pan. Drain away three quarters of the oil, and add pork, ginger, garlic, and salt to the other side of the pan. Stir-fry the pork and flavorings over high heat for 1½ minutes. Bring over the lobster pieces to turn and mix with the pork for 2 minutes.

Pour the chicken stock-soya-sherry mixture evenly over the lobster pieces and scatter the top with scallion or spring onion segments. When the contents begin to boil hard, turn the lobster pieces over a few times. Pour the cornflour mixture evenly over the pan and turn the contents over a few more times. Now drip the beaten egg evenly over the lobster and pork. As soon as the eggs set the dish is ready to serve.

Serve in a deep-sided, well-heated dish.

1 lobster (2 or 3 lb)
3–4 cloves garlic
3 slices root-ginger
3–4 stalks scallions or spring onions
5–6 tablespoons vegetable oil
¼ lb ground or minced pork
¼ pint High Broth, or good chicken stock
3 tablespoons dry sherry, or Chinese yellow wine
1 tablespoon soya sauce
1½ teaspoons sugar
1 tablespoon cornflour (blended in 3–4 tablespoons water)
2 tablespoons flour
2 eggs

Slow-cooked Steamed Duck with Mushrooms

Prepare duck by removing the oil sacs and stuffing the cavity with shredded ginger and spring onions cut into 1 inch segments. Soak mushroom in water for 20 minutes. Cut away the stalks.

Place duck and salt in a large casserole. Add water to cover the duck. Bring to the boil and simmer gently for 35 minutes. Skim away oil and impurities. Add mushrooms, soya sauce and sherry. Place the casserole in a steamer (or in a large boiler with $1\frac{1}{2}$ inches of water kept simmering) and steam or simmer for 2 hours.

Serve by bringing the casserole to the table. The steaming dish is very heart-warming in the autumn and very savory and delicious to the palate.

1 medium duck ($3\frac{1}{2}$ lb)
2 slices root-ginger
3 stalks scallions or spring onions
8 medium Chinese dried mushrooms
3–4 teaspoons salt
$1\frac{1}{2}$ tablespoons soya sauce
4–5 tablespoons dry sherry (or Chinese yellow wine)

Slow-simmered Sea Bass in Gingsen Soup

Shred and finely chop ginger. Clean fish and rub with salt, ginger and pepper. Leave to season for 1 hour.

Cut bacon (across lean and fat) and peppers into matchstick shreds. Soak mushrooms in water for $\frac{1}{2}$ hour and cut into similar shreds. Cut scallions or spring onions into 2 inch segments.

Place the fish in an oval or rectangular, deep-sided, heatproof dish. Add Gingsen Soup, vinegar, ginger and white wine. Cover the dish firmly with foil and place in a moderate oven at (350°F, 180°C or Gas No 4) for 25 minutes.

Lift the foil, turn the fish over and dress the top of the fish with the bacon, mushroom, scallions, (spring onions) and pepper strips. Return the dish to the oven to bake for a further 15 minutes.

Serve by bringing the dish to the table and removing the foil. This is a "semi-soup dish." The soup in the deep-sided dish can be drunk by the spoonful.

1 sea bass (2–3 lb)
2 slices root-ginger
2 teaspoons salt
pepper (to taste)
$\frac{1}{3}$ pint Gingsen Soup
$\frac{1}{4}$ pint white wine (dry)
$1\frac{1}{2}$ tablespoons wine vinegar
$\frac{1}{2}$ green pepper
$\frac{1}{2}$ red pepper
2 Chinese dried mushrooms
2 slices (rashers) bacon
2 stalks scallions or spring onions

Quick-fried Sliced Steak in Oyster Sauce (or with oysters)

This dish can be cooked with fresh oysters or with just the oyster sauce (the normal way in Chinese restaurants), but it is much more exciting with fresh oysters.

Chop and crush the garlic and ginger into fine grains. Cut the scallions or spring onions into 1 inch segments. Cut beef into very thin 2 × 1 inch slices. Remove the oysters from their shells and sprinkle them with salt and pepper to taste. Mix soya sauce, 1 tablespoon oil, the oyster sauce and the sherry until well blended. Add this mixture to the beef and oysters, rub it into the beef and leave to marinate for 15 minutes.

$1\frac{1}{4}$ lb beef steak (fillet)
6–8 medium oysters
1 teaspoon salt
pepper (to taste)
$1\frac{1}{2}$ tablespoons soya sauce
$1\frac{1}{2}$ tablespoons oyster sauce
$1\frac{1}{2}$ tablespoons vegetable oil
2 cloves garlic
2 slices root-ginger
3 stalks scallions or spring onions
$\frac{3}{4}$ tablespoons cornflour (blended in 4 tablespoons cold chicken stock)

Heat remaining oil in a large frying pan. When very hot add ginger, garlic and scallion (spring onion) segments. Turn them in the oil for $\frac{1}{2}$ minute over high heat. Tip the beef and oysters into the pan. Continue to turn and stir-fry over high heat for 2 minutes. Pour the blended cornflour into the pan. Turn and stir-fry for 1 more minute.

Serve in a well-heated dish.

Cherry Pork

This is a "sweet and sour" dish. For those who have a liking for the "sweet and sour" flavor, this is an excellent dish to include in any menu.

Cut pork into $\frac{1}{2}$ inch cubes. Rub with salt and dredge with flour (shake free of any excess flour). Remove the stalk and stone from the cherries. Mix the ingredients for the sauce until well blended.

Heat oil in a large frying pan or Chinese wok. When hot add the pork and stir-fry over high heat for $3\frac{1}{2}$ minutes. Drain away excess oil. Add soya sauce. Stir and turn the pork over a few times. Pour in the sauce mixture. Turn the heat down to medium and turn the pork slowly in the sauce until the latter begins to thicken and become translucent. Tip in the cherries and mix with the sauce and pork. Leave to cook gently for $2\frac{1}{2}$ minutes more.

Serve in a white or plain colored round serving dish.

$1\frac{1}{2}$ lb lean pork
$\frac{3}{4}$ lb pink or bright red cherries
2 tablespoons flour (for dredging the pork)
$1\frac{1}{2}$ teaspoons salt
$1\frac{1}{2}$ tablespoons soya sauce
6 tablespoons vegetable oil

For the sauce
2 tablespoons sugar
$2\frac{1}{2}$ tablespoons Chinese red vinegar
2 tablespoons cornflour (blended in 6 tablespoons water–add a little red coloring, if no red vinegar available)
$1\frac{1}{2}$ tablespoons tomato purée
4 tablespoons orange juice
$1\frac{1}{2}$ tablespoons soya sauce

THE IMPECUNIOUS LOVER

Chicken Soup-Noodle
Three Fried Eggs in Sweet and Sour Sauce
Steamed Pork Pudding with Cauliflower
Red-Cook Chicken Drumsticks with Chestnuts

As in the month of September, the impecunious lover will put up a brave front by serving four dishes for his dinner. In place of the customary congee, or rice gruel, he starts with a bowl of noodles prepared from half a duck or chicken carcass, which is decorated or garnished with a couple of tablespoonfuls of shredded ham and chicken meat. The dish acts both as the bulk food and soup of the meal.

Chicken Soup-Noodle

Boil the chicken carcass by simmering it slowly in $1\frac{2}{3}$ pints of water for 1 hour to produce 1 pint of chicken stock. Add salt and monosodium glutamate (or stock cube). Boil noodles for 5–6 minutes in a pan of boiling water to cook and loosen. Drain. Cut scallions or spring onions into coarse grains or shavings.

Add noodles and scallions or spring onions to the chicken stock to simmer for 3–4 minutes.

Divide the noodles and chicken broth into two equal bowls. Garnish with shredded ham and chicken and serve.

$\frac{1}{2}$ chicken carcass
1 teaspoon salt
$\frac{1}{4}$ teaspoon monosodium glutamate (or $\frac{1}{2}$ chicken stock cube)
$\frac{1}{4}$ lb Chinese egg noodles
2 stalks scallions or spring onions
1–2 tablespoons shredded ham
1–2 tablespoons cooked chicken meat

Three Fried Eggs in Sweet and Sour Sauce

Mix all the ingredients for the sauce until well blended. Place a flat, plain colored serving dish in the oven for a few minutes to warm.

Heat the sauce mixture in a small saucepan over medium heat. Stir until the mixture becomes thick and translucent. Heat oil in a frying pan, and fry the 3 eggs in the usual way.

Transfer the eggs from the pan on to the well-heated serving dish. Pour the sauce evenly over the eggs. The sauce is rich in color and helps to endow the dish with a feeling of extravagance.

3 eggs
4–5 tablespoons vegetable oil

For the sauce
$\frac{3}{4}$ tablespoon cornflour (with 4 tablespoons water)
$1\frac{1}{4}$ tablespoons soya sauce
$1\frac{1}{4}$ tablespoons tomato purée
1 tablespoon sugar
$1\frac{1}{2}$ tablespoons vinegar
2 tablespoons orange juice

Steamed Pork Pudding with Cauliflower

Chop the onion and pickles into coarse grains, and the garlic into fine grains. Add them to the pork, along with the cornflour, egg, salt, soya sauce, sherry, sugar and sesame oil. Stir and turn until they are well mixed. Break the cauliflower into individual flowerets.

Place the cauliflower at the bottom of a heatproof dish or basin. Pack the pork mixture in a thick layer over the top. Place the basin in a large saucepan in which 1–1½ inches of water is kept at a simmer. Do not allow any water to lap over the top of the dish or basin which should be at least 4 inches high. To be safe, the top of the basin may be covered with foil. Allow the "steaming" or double boiling to proceed for 1 hour, replenishing the water simmering in the saucepan when necessary.

Serve by bringing the basin or dish to the table.

⅓–½ lb minced pork
1 medium onion
1½ tablespoons chopped pickles
1½ tablespoons cornflour
1 egg
½ teaspoon salt
2 cloves garlic
1½ tablespoons soya sauce
1 tablespoon sherry
½ teaspoon sugar
2 teaspoons sesame oil
1 medium cauliflower

Red-Cook Chicken Drumsticks with Chestnuts

With only two people eating, this dish needs just a pair of drumsticks and 4 chestnuts, so the cost is minimal.

Remove the shell and membrane of the chestnuts.

Heat oil in a small saucepan. Dredge the drumsticks with flour, and fry in the oil in a frying pan until brown. Add the chestnuts, sugar, sherry, soya sauce and water. Cook over medium heat for 2 minutes.

Turn the contents into a medium serving bowl for the diners to help themselves. With four bowls (one bowl each of noodles) and one dish spread out on the table, the impecunious lover could feel that he is having a field day. Yet none of the dishes needs cost much at all.

2 chicken drumsticks
4 chestnuts
2 tablespoons soya sauce
2 tablespoons sherry
¼ teaspoon sugar
4–5 tablespoons water
2 tablespoons vegetable oil

THE LOVER IN A HURRY

Seafood Noodle Soup with Mushrooms
Quick-fried Beef with Scallions or Spring Onions
Stir-fry Breast of Chicken with Celery

The lover in a hurry should be able to serve his meal within 15–20 minutes. As rice would take 20 minutes to cook on its own, his best plan would be to serve a delicious noodle dish, laced in wine – which can be got up within 6–7 minutes – to be accompanied by two stir-fried dishes, either of which can be prepared and cooked within 4–5 minutes. (Much of the cooking of the two dishes can be done simultaneously.)

Seafood Noodle Soup with Mushrooms

Shred ginger. Cut onion and mushrooms into thin slices. Cut bacon into matchstick shreds.

Heat $\frac{3}{4}$ pint of water in a saucepan. As soon as it boils add noodles, stock cube and ginger. Leave to simmer. Simultaneously heat oil in a frying pan. Add onion and bacon. Stir-fry over high heat for 1 minute. Add mushrooms and shrimps. Continue to stir-fry over high heat for $2\frac{1}{2}$ minutes. Add sherry and leave the frying pan over the heat, while dividing the noodles and soup into two bowls.

Serve the two bowls of soup noodles garnished with the shrimps, bacon and mushrooms from the frying pan. This substantial dish should not take more than 6–7 minutes to cook – with practice not more than 5 minutes.

$\frac{1}{4}$–$\frac{1}{2}$ lb egg noodles
1 chicken stock cube
1–2 slices root-ginger

For garnish
1 onion
2 slices (rashers) bacon
$\frac{1}{4}$ lb frozen shrimps
4 medium/large button mushrooms
3 tablespoons vegetable oil
4–5 tablespoons dry sherry or white wine

Quick-fried Beef with Scallions or Spring Onions

Cut steak into a dozen thin slices. Add sugar, pepper (to taste), soya sauce and 1 tablespoon oil for marinade. Turn them around so that the marinade is well rubbed into the meat. Crush garlic and cut scallions or spring onions into 2 inch segments, while the remaining oil is being heated in a frying pan.

When the oil is hot, add garlic and scallions or spring onions. After turning them around a couple of times tip in the beef. Break the beef up and spread it out in the pan. Stir-fry and turn the ingredients together over high heat for $2\frac{1}{2}$ minutes, when the beef should be ready to serve. Serve in a well-heated dish.

1 lb beef steak
2 tablespoons soya sauce
pepper (to taste)
4 tablespoons vegetable oil
1 teaspoon sugar
3 stalks scallions or spring onions
2 cloves garlic

Stir-fry Breast of Chicken with Celery

Cut chicken meat into a dozen thin slices. Dredge with corn-flour, sprinkle with salt and pepper, and rub these into the chicken with the fingers. Clean and cut celery slantwise into 1 inch slices.

Heat oil in frying pan. When very hot add the celery and chicken. Stir and turn them over high heat for 2 minutes. Pour the soya sauce and sherry over the chicken and celery, and continue to stir-fry for 1 minute. Serve in a well-heated dish. Serving this dish together with the two previous dishes all in 15–20 minutes, the lover in a hurry could take a justifiable pride in his or her performance.

5–6 oz breast of chicken
1 tablespoon cornflour
1 teaspoon salt
pepper (to taste)
4 tablespoons vegetable oil
3–4 sticks celery
1 tablespoon light-colored soya sauce
2 tablespoons sherry

THE LOVER WITH TIME TO SPARE

Crouton-encrusted Shrimp or Prawn Balls with Plum Sauce and Aromatic
Salt and Pepper Dip
Lemon Chicken
Chicken-Gingsen Soup with Chrysanthemums
Smoked Spareribs
Duck and Cucumber Salad

To be perfect many Chinese deep-fried dishes, which are crispy, should be served with two types of dip on the table. One of these is the aromatic salt-and-pepper dip, which is made by mixing sea salt with freshly ground pepper and heating the mixture on a dry, hot pan for a couple of minutes until a distinct bouquet arises. This dip is served on the table in a saucer or small plate for the diners to dip in individual pieces of food. It almost adds an extra dimension to the morsels of food consumed. In contrast and as a balance, for similar crispy food and dishes, a thick fruity sauce – such as the plum sauce, ketchup, or hoisin sauce (obtainable from all Chinese food stores) – is served on the table in similar saucers. The diner can then be dipping one morsel of food in the salt-and-pepper mix, and another in the fruity dip, or alternatively enjoy the rare experience of dipping a single crispy piece of food on one side in the salt-and-pepper and on the other in the fruity dip.

Crouton-encrusted Shrimp or Prawn Balls with Plum Sauce and Aromatic Salt-and-Pepper Dip

Make croutons by dicing bread into tiny $\frac{1}{4}$ inch cubes, heating in a moderate oven for 7–8 minutes, and leaving to cool. Chop pork fat and shrimp (prawn) meat into fine pieces with a pair of very sharp choppers (if possible Chinese). Cut water chestnuts and scallions or spring onions into coarse grains or shavings. Mix these ingredients together with salt, cornflour and $1\frac{1}{2}$ beaten eggs into a paste. Form the paste into $1\frac{1}{2}$ inch diameter balls. Roll these balls over the croutons so that each one is covered evenly and firmly with a layer of croutons.

Heat oil in the deep-fryer, or a saucepan (there should be at least 2 pints of oil). When hot, a breadcrumb should sizzle in it. Add one-quarter of the balls to fry for $2\frac{1}{2}$ minutes. Remove

1 slice bread
$\frac{3}{4}$ lb shrimp or prawn meat
$\frac{1}{4}$ lb pork fat
oil for deep frying
4 pieces water chestnut
1 teaspoon salt
1 tablespoon cornflour
2 eggs
2 stalks scallions or spring onions

with perforated spoon and put aside, and repeat with the other shrimp balls. When all the balls have been fried once, put them all into the hot oil for a final frying for just one minute. Remove to drain quickly on absorbent paper.

These crispy balls should be served on a well-heated serving dish, accompanied by the 2–3 dips described above, including the aromatic salt-and-pepper dip.

Lemon Chicken

Lemon chicken is a dish that exploits the appeal of "hot-saltiness and sourness."

Cut chicken meat from the bone into $1\frac{1}{2} \times 1\frac{1}{2}$ inch strips. Cut ginger into shreds and chop into fine grains. Add ginger, salt and cornflour to chicken. Mix them all together thoroughly and leave to season for 30 minutes. Soak mushrooms in water for 30 minutes, remove stalks and cut caps into matchstick shreds. Cut peppers into similar shreds, and scallions or spring onions into 2 inch segments. Squeeze the juice from 1 lemon (or $1\frac{1}{2}$ lemons, if you wish the sourness of the dish to be more pronounced).

Heat the oil in a large frying pan. When very hot add the chicken, spread out in the pan to stir-fry over high heat for $2\frac{1}{2}$ minutes. Remove and drain. Pour away all the oil except for 2 tablespoons. Add the shredded mushrooms and chili pepper to the pan. Stir them around over high heat for $\frac{1}{4}$ minute. Add the shredded sweet pepper, scallions or spring onions and lemon peel. Turn and stir them around for $\frac{1}{2}$ minute. Add soya sauce, sugar and chicken stock. Stir until the contents froth up into a high boil. Return the chicken to the pan to mix and stir with the other ingredients. Pour the lemon juice and the sherry over the contents of the pan. When the contents boil again turn them over a few times.

Serve in a deep-sided, well-heated dish. The hot-sourness of this well-spiced dish is of great appeal to many palates.

1 medium chicken
3 slices root-ginger
2–3 teaspoons salt
$1\frac{1}{2}$ tablespoons cornflour
4–5 large Chinese dried mushrooms
1 red sweet pepper
2 green hot chili peppers
3 stalks scallions or spring onions
2 medium lemons
lemon peel (shredded outer skin from 2 lemons)
juice from 1 lemon
2 tablespoons soya sauce
2 teaspoons sugar
4 tablespoons chicken stock
2 tablespoons dry sherry
$\frac{1}{4}$ pint vegetable oil

Chicken-Gingsen Soup with Chrysanthemums

Chrysanthemum petals are often put into Chinese dishes to celebrate the season and the harvest.

Cut chicken meat into thin $1 \times \frac{1}{2}$ inch slices. Dredge with cornflour and wet with egg white. Soak mushrooms for $\frac{1}{2}$ hour. Remove stalks and cut caps into quarters. Pull the petals from the chrysanthemums. Heat stock in a saucepan. Add Gingsen Soup. When hot, add mushrooms, salt and monosodium glutamate. Allow the contents to simmer gently for 3 minutes. Add the chicken and allow the contents to simmer for 3

1 pint chicken stock or High Broth
$1\frac{1}{2}$ teaspoons salt
$\frac{1}{2}$ pint Gingsen Soup
$\frac{1}{4}$ lb chicken breast meat
$\frac{1}{2}$ tablespoon cornflour
1 egg white
3 medium Chinese dried mushrooms

minutes. Just before dishing, sprinkle the top of the soup with chrysanthemum petals. Serve immediately (otherwise the petals may become bitter) in individual bowls (there should be sufficient here for 3–4 bowls).

4 small chrysanthemum heads
½ teaspoon flavor powder or monosodium glutamate

Smoked Spareribs

Cut spareribs into individual ribs. Parboil for 4–5 minutes and drain. Cut onion into thin slices, shred ginger, crush garlic. Place ribs in a casserole. Add ginger, garlic, onion, soya sauce, sugar, "five spice" and water. Bring to the boil, add sherry, stock cube and Superior Gravy. Reduce heat to low and leave contents to simmer for 1 hour, turning the contents over every 20 minutes. Remove from heat, and leave the ribs to stand in the gravy or marinade overnight.

2 lb pork spareribs (ribs from rib-cage)
2 medium onions
3 slices root ginger
3 cloves garlic
2 tablespoons soya sauce
2 teaspoons sugar
1 tablespoon mixed "five spice"
1 chicken stock cube
¼ pint water
4 tablespoons dry sherry
4 tablespoons Superior Gravy

Mix the tea, sawdust and pine needles, and place the mixture at the bottom of a very large, old saucepan (to be kept specially for the purpose). Place a piece of thick wood (1 × 1½ inches thick) in the bottom. Pile the spareribs spaced out in an enamel dish and place it on top of the piece of wood. Place the saucepan over high heat until the tea/sawdust/pine needle mixture begins to smoke heavily. Reduce the heat to medium, cover the top of the pan firmly with a lid, and leave the pan over the heat for a further 3 minutes. Remove from heat but do not open the lid for at least 10–12 minutes.

Remove the ribs from the "smoking pan." Brush them with sesame oil. Arrange them on a heatproof dish. Insert the dish into a hot oven (425°F, 200°C or Gas No 6) for 10 minutes.

For smoking
3 tablespoons dried tea (used)
3 tablespoons sawdust
3 tablespoons pine needles (dried)
2 tablespoons sesame oil

Serve either in the heatproof dish or another serving dish. Can be served and eaten either hot or cold. The smoked taste should be very distinct.

Duck and Cucumber Salad

Cut ginger into fine threads. Cut meat from roast duck into large matchstick shreds. Sprinkle salt and ginger over the duck, and toss them together. Trim the end off the cucumber. Cut half of it into thin slices and the other half into similar shreds as the duck.

½ roast duck (about 1½ lb)
2 slices root-ginger
1 teaspoon salt
1 large cucumber

Pile the sliced cucumber in the center of a large serving dish. Lay the shredded cucumber in four "legs" spreading out from the center to the edge of the dish. Place half the shredded duck on top of the cucumber in the center and the rest of it between the "legs" of cucumber.

Mix the ingredients for the sauce until well blended. Pour the sauce evenly over the chicken and cucumber. Serve as a starter or in conjunction with the other dishes in the menu.

For the sauce

3–4 teaspoons dry mustard
$1\frac{1}{2}$ tablespoons soya sauce
$1\frac{1}{2}$ tablespoons wine vinegar
$\frac{1}{2}$ teaspoon salt
$1\frac{1}{2}$ teaspoons sugar
$1\frac{1}{2}$ tablespoons dry sherry
$2\frac{1}{2}$ tablespoons High Broth (or good chicken stock)
$\frac{1}{4}$ teaspoon monosodium glutamate
3 teaspoons sesame oil

November

THE AFFLUENT LOVER

Pâté de Foie Gras
Pheasant in Cream Sauce
Potatoes Maître d'Hôtel
Sea Kale
Pears in Red Wine

November is the ideal month for serving game, and none of it is more delicious than a plump pheasant. The method of marinating and slow roasting is an easy one when you don't want to be tied to punctuality. When you are ready to eat, you should carve the pheasant, and Mouli or sieve the sauce. Then arrange the best pheasant pieces on a warm dish with the sauce poured over and a piece of foil laid on top, and keep in the oven while you savor the smooth pâté, so wickedly luxurious, with its hidden truffles and rich fat. Reheat the maître d'hôtel butter for the potatoes and bring the pheasant and sea kale from the oven. Then you are all set for a gastronomic treat. This meal is worthy of a very fine claret. Nothing more needs to be done, but to sit back and enjoy the luscious pears and the acclaim of your loved one.

Pâté de Foie Gras

Don't buy one of the ordinary liver pâtés which are sold everywhere, but the true foie gras, which comes in china jars or tins. If you buy a tin, turn out the foie gras and serve in slices on each plate. The jar, on the other hand, is nice enough looking to serve from. Make plenty of hot toast just before you eat.

Pheasant in Cream Sauce

Peel and slice the onion, and scrape and slice the carrots and celery. Put in a basin with all the other ingredients for the marinade, and put the pheasant into soak for 2 or 3 hours, spooning some of the liquid over the bird occasionally. Alternatively, you can leave the pheasant to marinate overnight if it suits your plans better.

    Take the bird out of the marinade and cover the breast with bacon slices (rashers) tied lightly in place with string. Pour all the vegetables and liquid from the basin of marinade round the pheasant, cover with foil and slow roast for $1\frac{3}{4}$ hours in a very

1 pheasant
6 slices (rashers) fat bacon
1 teaspoon flour
$\frac{1}{4}$ pint cream
squeeze of lemon juice

moderate oven (325°F, 170°C or Gas No 3). Remove the foil 15 minutes before the end of the cooking time. Put the cream into a small bowl, stir in the flour and squeeze of lemon juice.

To serve, remove the bacon and string, carve the pheasant and arrange the best pieces on a warm dish. Rub the vegetables and juices from the pan through a food mill, and heat in a small saucepan with the cream mixture. Stir until the sauce thickens smoothly, then pour over the pheasant.

For the marinade
1 onion
2 carrots
2 sticks celery
1 bay leaf
1 teaspoon salt
4 peppercorns
4 tablespoons wine vinegar
4 tablespoons water

Potatoes Maître d'Hôtel

Boil the potatoes in their skins for about 15 minutes. Do not overcook. Test with the point of a sharp knife; it should sink in with a little pressure. Drain the potatoes and, when cool enough to handle, peel away the skins. Cut into even slices and set aside. Melt the butter in a pan and gently fry the onion until soft but not brown. At this stage you may set the pan aside until you are ready to dish up. There is usually a place at the back of the stove, or in a plate-warming compartment, in which the potatoes and the pan of onion would keep just warm.

To serve, draw the pan of butter and onion over the heat, stir in the parsley, season and heat thoroughly. Then add the potatoes and toss them in the maître d'hôtel butter.

$\frac{3}{4}$ lb small potatoes
1 oz butter
1 level tablespoon finely chopped onion
1 level tablespoon finely chopped parsley
salt and pepper

Sea Kale

Trim away any roots or damaged stems, and wash the sea kale thoroughly. Boil in salted water for 30 minutes, drain and set aside. Thickly butter a small ovenproof dish and arrange the sea kale in it. Cover with foil and place in the bottom of the oven 15 minutes before the pheasant is ready to serve, (i.e. when you remove the foil from the pheasant).

1 lb sea kale
butter

Pears in Red Wine

Peel the pears thinly and leave them whole. Choose a small pan in which they will fit and put the pears in on their sides, with the sugar and cinnamon. Pour in the wine, cover with a lid, bring to the boil and simmer for 10 minutes. Turn the pears over and simmer for 5 or 10 minutes longer, until they are tender. Lift the pears carefully into a deep serving dish, and continue to boil the liquid in the pan until reduced to a light syrup. Spoon the syrup over the pears, cool and chill. Serve with thick cream.

2 ripe pears
4 oz sugar
$\frac{1}{2}$ teaspoon cinnamon
$\frac{1}{2}$ pint red wine

THE IMPECUNIOUS LOVER

Haddock Pâté
Rabbit with Mustard Sauce
Lentil Purée
Apples with Caramel and Orange

The basic ingredients of this menu are cheap: smoked haddock, rabbit, lentils and apples. But the clever cook, with the help of a dash of cream for the pâté and rabbit, and the incentive to cook imaginatively, can produce a dinner party for two that suggests a far more lavish way of life, and is an economic version of the affluent lover's menu. All can be prepared in advance; the main course will keep waiting happily in a warm oven and only requires the addition of a spoonful of cream and chopped parsley when brought quickly to a brisk heat before serving.

A small white jug of vivid yellow daisies should not knock holes in your pocket and perhaps you could muster china or napkins that will play up the theme of autumn yellows and russets. The pâté, the lentils and the caramel- and orange-garnished apples will help your color scheme of mellow fruitfulness.

Haddock Pâté

Rinse the haddock fillet and put in a saucepan with a cupful of water. Bring to the boil, and cook gently for 10 minutes. Drain and cool. Remove the skin, and put the fish in a basin. Add the melted butter and mash well together. Blend the fish mixture in an electric blender until smooth, or rub through a fine sieve. Stir in the lemon juice and Worcestershire sauce and add a grinding of pepper to the mixture. Lightly whip the cream, first adding a little milk if it is very thick, and fold into the fish mixture. Spoon into a small bowl or jar and chill until firm. Run a little melted butter over the top of the pâté and return to the refrigerator. Serve with hot toast or brown bread and butter.

$\frac{1}{4}$ lb smoked haddock fillet
$\frac{1}{2}$ oz butter
squeeze of lemon juice
a few drops of Worcestershire sauce
freshly milled pepper
2 tablespoons heavy (double) cream
1 tablespoon melted butter
bread and butter

Rabbit with Mustard Sauce

Marinate the rabbit joints in a deep dish and cover with equal parts of vinegar and water, with a bay leaf, 2 or 3 peppercorns and a sprig of thyme or rosemary. Leave overnight. Take out the rabbit joints and pat dry. Melt the dripping in a heavy pan and fry the rabbit joints until brown on all sides. Peel and chop the onions finely and chop the bacon. Lift out the rabbit and add the bacon and onions to the pan. Fry gently until beginning to brown and soften. Shake in the flour and stir. Then add the warmed stock, stir well until boiling and smooth. Tip back the pieces of rabbit, season with salt and pepper and add the mustard. Cover the pan and simmer gently for 1 hour; dish the rabbit and keep warm. Add the cream to the sauce in the pan, stir and cover. When ready to serve, bring the sauce close to boiling point and spoon over the rabbit.

$\frac{3}{4}$ lb rabbit joints
marinade – see recipe
$\frac{1}{2}$ oz dripping
2 medium onions
2 bacon slices (rashers)
$\frac{1}{2}$ tablespoon flour
$\frac{1}{2}$ pint stock
salt and pepper to taste
2 large teaspoons French mustard
1 tablespoon cream

Lentil Purée

After soaking the lentils overnight, rinse them in fresh water. Peel and chop the onion and scrape and slice the carrot. Place all the vegetables in a saucepan, cover with cold water and add a seasoning of salt and the dried tarragon. Bring to the boil and simmer for 40–50 minutes until the lentils are soft. Drain and rub the vegetables through a sieve or food mill. Reserve a little of the cooking liquid. Melt the butter in a clean pan, add the lentil purée and a seasoning of ginger and black pepper. When ready to serve, reheat with a little of the reserved liquid to keep the purée moist, and serve nice and hot.

$\frac{1}{2}$ pint lentils, soaked overnight
$\frac{1}{2}$ onion
1 small carrot
pinch of salt
$\frac{1}{2}$ teaspoon dried tarragon
1 oz butter
$\frac{1}{2}$ teaspoon ground ginger
freshly milled black pepper

Apples with Caramel and Orange

Peel and quarter the apples. Put the water and sugar in a pan; heat and stir until the sugar dissolves, then boil briskly for 3 minutes. Put the apples into the syrup and simmer gently for 10 minutes. Take off the heat and allow to get cold. Pare off a few curls of the orange rind, cut into fine shreds and boil up in a small pan of water for 4 or 5 minutes. Drain and rinse in cold water. Peel the orange carefully, removing all white pith, and slice into thin rounds.

Make a caramel sauce by melting the sugar in a dry pan over high heat until the sugar turns golden brown, draw off the heat, and pour on the cold water, taking care as it will bubble furiously. Return the pan to the heat and stir until the sauce is smooth and golden brown. Pour quickly into a greased tin, and allow to set.

Spoon the apples into a china or earthenware dish, with some of their syrup. Arrange the orange slices on top of the apples. Break the caramel up into little fragments, scatter over the fruit and garnish with the little shreds of orange peel. Chill until ready to serve.

2 or 3 dessert apples
1 teacup water
3 oz sugar
1 orange

For the caramel
2 oz sugar
2 tablespoons water

THE LOVER IN A HURRY

Pâté de Maison
Lamb Chops with Marsala or Brown Sherry
or
Roast Partridge
Tomato Salad
Ice Cream with Kissel

You will have to do a bit of cheating with this menu, but some skillful short cuts are worth knowing. A piece of continental liver sausage can closely resemble a home-made pâté when mixed with brandy and served in a little jar. Roast partridge is given as an alternative to the dish of lamb chops, as it will take you no longer to prepare, but the choice will depend on how near you are to a shop that will sell a brace of partridges, and on what sort of budget you are catering. Both dishes are extremely good, and the tomato salad and a crusty loaf made hot in the oven would go equally well with either. Kissel, the delicious Austrian compôte of dark red fruits is always thickened with arrow-root, which gives it a special consistency. This consistency can be achieved by choosing as one of your canned fruits a pie filling; the jellied syrup when stirred with the juice of the other two fruits becomes just the right thickness, and a spoonful of red wine completes the fraud. All is fair in love and the kitchen.

A bottle of St. Amour (Beaujolais) would help to get your message across and there is nothing fraudulent about it.

Pâté de Maison

Remove the skin from the sausage and place in a small basin. Trickle in the brandy and stir and mash with a wooden spoon, so that the brandy is thoroughly mixed and the pâté moist, but not wet. Turn into a small earthenware pot or jar and chill. Serve with hot toast or a crisp French loaf and butter.

6 oz continental liver sausage
scant tablespoon brandy or sherry
French bread or hot toast

Lamb Chops with Marsala or Brown Sherry

Trim the chops and roll in seasoned flour. Heat the butter in a frying pan and fry the chops until both sides are browned, then lift out the chops and place in a small ovenproof dish with a lid.

2 large lamb chops
seasoned flour
1 oz butter

Take a scant tablespoon from the seasoned flour and stir this into the butter in the pan. When smooth, add the Marsala and the stock. Bring to the boil, stirring all the time until the sauce is smooth and thick. Remove from the heat and pour over the chops, cover and place in the center of a moderate oven (350°F, 180°C or Gas No 4) and cook for 25 minutes.

2 tablespoons Marsala or brown sherry
¼ pint stock, made with a bouillon cube
salt and pepper

Alternative Roast Partridge

Cover the breasts of each bird with bacon slices, spread the butter over a roasting tin, set the partridges in the tin and place in a hot oven (400°F, 200°C or Gas No 6) for 25 minutes. To serve, remove the bacon, de-glaze the roasting tin with 3 tablespoons water and 2 tablespoons red wine (taken from the bottle you will probably be serving), boil up, and serve in a sauceboat as gravy.

2 plump partridges
4 bacon slices (rashers)
2 oz butter

For the gravy
2 tablespoons red wine
3 tablespoons water

Tomato Salad

Skin and slice the tomatoes and put them in a dish with the salt and pepper and a pinch of sugar. Mix with a good French dressing.

4 tomatoes
salt and pepper
pinch of sugar
French dressing

Ice Cream with Kissel

Turn out the fruits into a glass bowl and stir gently together until the juices are completely mingled. Lastly, stir in the wine. Serve at room temperature with the best vanilla ice cream you can buy.

1 small can raspberries
1 small can black cherries
1 small can blackcurrant pie filling
1 tablespoon red wine
vanilla ice cream

THE LOVER WITH TIME TO SPARE

Melon Cocktail
Ununass Pullow
Spinach Turned in Butter
Basbousa Bil Loz

This menu should be prepared in an atmosphere of unhurried, loving care, and by the time the doorbell rings, all will be ready, and the cook, unfettered by any activities in the kitchen, able to receive the eagerly awaited guest with an untroubled mind and open arms.

The melon fruit cocktail looks delightful and is a refreshing prelude to the early Indian dish of rice with sweet and sour spicy meat. This dish will wait accommodatingly over a low heat, while giving an exotic Eastern fragrance to the kichen. Spinach, previously cooked and drained, will reheat in a generous amount of butter with a hint of nutmeg, and come to the table tender and succulent. The little Persian dessert is flavored with almonds and lemon juice and should be served cool, but not chilled; it adds another Oriental touch to an unusual menu.

An arrangement of fruit and nuts in a really beautiful bowl or dish would look as attractive as any flowers. Later, a refreshing pot of China or Jasmine tea would be a delicate alternative to coffee. Depending on your capacity for exotic fragrance, a few gently smoldering joss-sticks offstage could add to the atmosphere of Eastern warmth and hospitality.

Melon Cocktail

Cut the melon into quarters and remove the seeds. Cut the flesh into cubes, or into balls with a melon scoop or vegetable baller. Tip the melon balls into a basin and sprinkle with sugar and ginger. Add the grated rind and strained juice of the orange and mix gently together. Leave to stand for several hours, then chill before serving.

1 small cantaloup or ripe honeydew melon
2 oz sugar
1 teaspoon ground ginger
finely grated rind and juice of 1 small orange

Ununass Pullow

This is a very delicious sweet-sour dish. Half the pineapple flesh is cooked in a light syrup as a final garnish to the meat; the rest is cooked with spices added to the syrup, until it is brown and sticky, then combined with the meat to give a fresh chutney flavor.

Trim and cut the meat into small, thick slices. Peel and slice the onion. Place the meat, onion, water, ginger, salt, coriander and 2 teaspoons of melted clarified butter into a saucepan. Bring to the boil, cover and simmer for 1 hour. When cooked, strain the gravy from the meat into another saucepan and set aside for cooking the rice. Heat 1 tablespoon of the remaining butter in a frying pan. Add the meat and onion mixture and fry gently until the mixture begins to brown, turning the meat pieces to fry on each side.

Meanwhile prepare the pineapple mixture. Dissolve the sugar in the water and lemon juice in a small pan and bring to the boil. Pare the rind off the pineapple and cut the flesh into slices. Put half the pineapple slices into the syrup, cover and boil for 15 minutes. Remove the fruit and reserve for the garnish. Add the remaining pineapple slices to the syrup, this time with the ground cloves, cumin, cardamoms and cinnamon added. Boil, with the lid off, until the syrup has nearly evaporated, and the mixture is sticky and brown.

Transfer the meat and onions from the frying pan to the saucepan of spicy pineapple. Stir together, and keep over a very low heat until needed.

Bring the gravy that was reserved for cooking the rice to the boil, add the washed rice and cook for 15 minutes. The gravy should all be absorbed by the rice.

Dish up the meat and spoon the cooked rice over. Pour over the remaining clarified butter – about two teaspoonfuls. Garnish with the cooked pineapple slices and serve. Or keep in a low oven until ready.

¾ lb boned shoulder or leg of lamb
1 small onion
½ pint water
1 slice green ginger, cut into strips
½ teaspoon salt
1 teaspoon ground coriander
2 oz clarified butter

For the pineapple and spiced syrup mixture
1 oz sugar
¼ pint water
1 teaspoon lemon juice
½ small fresh pineapple
pinch of ground cloves
1 small teaspoon ground cumin
2 cardamom seeds, peeled and crushed
½ teaspoon ground cinnamon
3 oz long grain rice

Basbousa Bil Loz

Heat the sugar, water and lemon juice in a pan. Stir until the sugar is dissolved, then boil for 3 minutes.

Melt the butter in a second saucepan; add the almonds and semolina. Stir together and fry gently until golden. Stir in the syrup slowly and cook over gentle heat until the mixture thickens; this takes about 5 minutes. Remove from the heat and allow to cool for a few moments, stirring occasionally to

3 oz sugar
½ pint water
juice of 1 lemon
1 oz butter
1 oz blanched and chopped almonds
1 oz semolina (farina)

prevent a skin forming. Pour into small individual pots, and serve cool, but not chilled.

A few toasted almonds and a spoonful of whipped cream makes an attractive topping to each little pot of this almond and lemon-flavored dessert.

December

THE AFFLUENT LOVER

Lobster Mayonnaise
Hunter's Beef
Lettuce and Watercress Salad
Fresh Pineapple with Kirsch

A lovely full-bodied burgundy would be right with this menu, with perhaps a glass of dry white wine to go with the lobster. Set the scene for some pre-Christmas revelry, an arrangement of white or red flowers tucked into shiny dark leaves. Red or green candles, your silver polished, yourself beautifully dressed, your dinner a triumph. Celebrate with this sophisticated food – and a pursuit as old as time.

Lobster Mayonnaise

Crack the lobster claws, pick out all the meat and take the meat from the tail. Discard the small bag or stomach in the head and the dark line running down the tail, but use the brown creamy mixture in the head. Put this with the white meat into a basin, cut the flesh into small pieces and toss with the lemon juice and salt and pepper and leave to marinate.

Wash out the lobster shells and dry carefully. Blend the lobster meat with the mayonnaise and spoon into the shells. Decorate each half with 2 or 3 slices of cucumber and a tiny sprinkling of cayenne pepper.

1 cooked lobster, cut in two halves
juice of $\frac{1}{2}$ lemon
salt and freshly milled pepper
3 tablespoons mayonnaise
a few slices cucumber
cayenne pepper

Hunter's Beef

Trim any fat from the meat, and cut into neat cubes. Heat the oil and butter together in a large saucepan and drop in the meat, brown quickly and evenly on all sides. Lift out the meat and reduce the heat. Peel and finely slice the onion and add to the fat in the pan; sauté for two or three minutes, then shake in the flour. Stir while the flour browns, then add the wine and tomato purée. Peel and crush the garlic and add to the mixture in the pan, then stir in the stock. Bring to the boil, stirring constantly. Finally, add the meat and reduce the heat to very low. Cover the pan with a tight-fitting lid and allow to simmer very slowly for 40 minutes. Then add the trimmed and wiped mush-

1 lb rump steak
1 tablespoon oil
$\frac{1}{2}$ oz butter
1 small onion
$\frac{1}{2}$ tablespoon flour
3 tablespoons red wine
1 teaspoon tomato purée
1 small clove garlic
$\frac{1}{4}$ pint strong stock
$\frac{1}{4}$ lb button mushrooms

rooms, and simmer for a further 10 minutes. The pan may now be drawn aside to wait, then brought again to the boil. If the sauce needs to thicken, dish the meat and boil the sauce rapidly to reduce a little. Serve with fresh bread.

Lettuce and Watercress Salad

Remove any limp or damaged leaves from the lettuce and pick over the watercress, selecting the best sprigs. Wash both lettuce and watercress in several waters, then shake dry. Peel and slice the cucumber thinly. Toss the lettuce and watercress in a French dressing and arrange in a salad bowl. Arrange the cucumber slices round the edge of the bowl.

1 lettuce
1 bunch watercress
$\frac{1}{4}$ cucumber
French dressing

Fresh Pineapple with Kirsch

Cut the top and bottom from the pineapple. Stand firmly upright and cut into quarters lengthways with a sharp knife. Cut the flesh from each quarter, rather as if it were a slice of melon, then cut away the core from each slice. Cut the flesh into bite-sized pieces and arrange as much as you require in a serving dish. Sprinkle with sugar and Kirsch, and chill until ready to serve.

1 ripe pineapple
1 tablespoon sugar
2 tablespoons Kirsch

THE IMPECUNIOUS LOVER

Borscht
Pork and Red Cabbage Stew
Boiled or Mashed Potatoes
Fresh Orange Jelly

The borscht, and the pork and red cabbage stew, are warming and satisfying for a cold December evening. Draw the curtains to shut out the winter night, and use a few cheerful red candles to shed an aura of warmth and welcome. The soup reheats so quickly, and the stew goes simmering on, that you have no need to think of the kitchen, however long your welcome lasts. To round off a filling meal, the cool orange jelly is light and refreshing.

Borscht

Peel the beetroot and grate on the coarsest grater. Heat the butter in a saucepan, peel and finely chop the onion and cook gently in the butter until soft, but not brown. Shake in the flour and stir; then slowly pour in the stock, bring to the boil and stir constantly until the liquid thickens. Tip in the grated beetroot and season with salt and plenty of pepper. Cover the pan and simmer gently for about 10 minutes. Rub the soup through a fine sieve, or food mill, over a clean pan. When ready to serve, reheat the soup gently, and swirl in the sour cream at the last moment. Pour into two warmed bowls.

1 medium cooked beetroot
½ oz butter
½ onion
½ level tablespoon flour
¾ pint stock
salt and pepper
2 tablespoons sour cream or fresh cream with a squeeze of lemon

Pork and Red Cabbage Stew

Choose belly pork that is as unfatty as possible – it does vary greatly. Trim off the rind and cut into small chunks. Melt the dripping in a heavy pan and brown the pork chunks in it for at least 15 minutes, turning them from time to time until the fat runs freely. Pour off the surplus fat to leave about half a tablespoon. Peel and chop the onion and soften it for a few minutes in the fat with the pork. Stir in the flour, add the beer and bring it to the boil, stirring all the time. Add the vinegar, coriander, tomato purée, caraway seeds and salt and pepper. Cut the cabbage into quarters, trim away the hard core, and wash thoroughly, then shred very finely and add to the pan, cover and allow to simmer gently for at least 1½ hours.

¼ lb unsalted belly pork
½ tablespoon dripping
1 medium onion
½ tablespoon flour
¼ pint pale ale or lager
3 tablespoons vinegar
1 heaped teaspoon coriander
1 teaspoon tomato purée
¼ teaspoon caraway seeds
salt
pepper
1 small red cabbage

You can cook this stew in advance and reheat it, or leave it cooking for up to 2 hours without spoiling in any way.

Serve with boiled or mashed potatoes and a well-chilled lager to enhance the Germanic flavorings.

Fresh Orange Jelly

Measure the gelatine and water into a small pan and leave to soak for 5 minutes. Then add the sugar. Set the pan over a low heat and stir until the sugar and gelatine have dissolved and the liquid is clear. Remove from the heat and stir in the orange and lemon juice. When cool, pour into a small glass bowl, or individual glasses, and leave until set firm. Serve with cream if you wish.

¼ oz powdered gelatine
4 tablespoons cold water
1 tablespoon sugar
¼ pint fresh or canned orange juice
juice of ½ lemon
cream (optional)

THE LOVER IN A HURRY

Cold Tomato Soup with Yogurt
Fried Pork Fillet
Cauliflower Sprigs
Lemon Syllabub

You can prepare this menu very quickly: the refreshing chilled soup needs no cooking, the hot pork, brown, rich and buttery, can be fried in ten minutes, and the syllabub, very light and creamy, flavored with wine and lemon, takes only 5 or 6 minutes to prepare. Or you can prepare it 2 or 3 days in advance.

The preparations for dinner should leave you time to set the table, with perhaps a glass of sweetly scented spring flowers which are temptingly displayed by shops and stalls at this time of year. They will look beautiful by candlelight, their fragility enhanced by the harsh weather outside. A howling wind or lashing rain will likewise enhance the warm intimacy of an evening *à deux*.

Cold Tomato Soup with Yogurt

Mix all the ingredients, except the dried herbs, in a basin, then pour into individual bowls and chill in the refrigerator. Before serving, sprinkle a pinch of basil or chervil on to each bowl of soup.

$\frac{1}{2}$ pint tomato juice
1 small carton yogurt
juice of $\frac{1}{2}$ lemon
1 teaspoon crushed garlic, or grated onion
salt and pepper
dried basil, or chervil

Fried Pork Fillet

Trim the fillet, and cut across in thick slices. Cover with a clean cloth, and flatten the pieces a little by beating with a rolling pin. Mix the egg lightly on a large plate and dip each piece of pork in egg; shake off the surplus, and then dip in the bread-crumbs. At this stage you can leave the crumbed pork on a wire rack or clean plate.

Put a good knob of butter into a large pan and leave ready in a warm place. Just before you want to eat, heat the butter, drop in the pieces of pork and fry for 5 minutes on each side until nicely browned. Dish the pork with the pan juices and keep warm while you drink the soup. Serve with lemon wedges.

$\frac{3}{4}$ lb pork fillet
1 egg
browned breadcrumbs
butter for frying
1 lemon for garnish

Cauliflower Sprigs

Break a small, fresh cauliflower into sprigs and cook in boiling, salted water for 7 minutes. Do this while the pork is frying. Drain, and arrange on a warm dish, pour a little melted butter over the cauliflower sprigs, and dust with paprika.

If you have time, a dish of creamed potatoes would be nice, or some potato crisps warmed in the oven.

1 cauliflower
salt
melted butter
paprika

Lemon Syllabub

Measure the wine into a basin, add the grated rind and strained lemon juice. Add the sugar and stir with a wooden spoon until it has dissolved. Stir in the cream, and then whip with a rotary whisk until the syllabub stands in a soft peak. Spoon into individual glasses and stand in a cool place.

3 tablespoons white wine
finely grated rind and juice of
$\frac{1}{2}$ lemon
1 level tablespoon sugar
$\frac{1}{4}$ pint heavy (double) cream

THE LOVER WITH TIME TO SPARE

Salted Almonds
Daube de Boeuf Provençale
Potato Croquettes
Small Brussels Sprouts and Chestnuts
Bavarian Cream with Praline

If you can stage a winter evening in the country, nothing is more romantic than a blazing log fire, with one or two apple logs to give out the most lovely fragrance. Your home-toasted almonds, served warm, can be nibbled with an apéritif while you toast yourselves by the fire. The Daube de Boeuf is improved by being kept waiting, and when you are ready for dinner, the sprouts will cook in 7 minutes in a pan of boiling water, with the chestnuts which you cooked previously added. Reheat the potato croquettes at the same time. The praline dessert can be made the evening before.

Take your coffee and liqueurs to the firelight.

Salted Almonds

Plunge the almonds into a pan of boiling water for 1 minute, drain, and peel away the skins. Rub the almonds dry in a clean tea towel. Heat the butter in a small frying pan, and shake some salt crystals on to a plate. When the butter is hot, drop in the almonds and fry them, shaking the pan and turning the almonds with a spoon until they are nutty brown on all sides. Lift from the pan with a slotted spoon, and roll in sea salt until lightly coated. It is nice to warm them slightly before eating.

2 oz unblanched almonds
sea salt crystals
knob of butter

Daube de Boeuf Provençale

The amount of beef given is more than you will need for one meal, but it cooks best in a large piece, and the dish is usually even better when reheated the next day.

Trim the meat and tie in a neat shape. Peel and slice the onions. Heat the oil in a pan and sauté the onions until golden. Cut the pork or bacon into cubes, add to the onions in the pan and cook until brown. Peel the tomatoes, chop them roughly and discard the seeds. Scrape and slice the carrot and peel and crush the garlic. Put all these into a deep casserole with the onions and diced pork. Finally brown the beef in the frying pan, and when browned on all sides, lift into the casserole with the vegetables. Add the orange rind, bouquet garni and a seasoning of salt and pepper. Warm the wine in a small pan and pour over the contents in the casserole. Cover closely with foil and then the lid and cook in a low oven (275°F, 140°C or Gas No 1) for 3 or 4 hours.

To serve, remove the bouquet garni and orange rind, lift the meat on to a warm dish, and pour the sauce and vegetables round the beef.

2 lb lean top rump, or stewing beef
2 small onions
2 tablespoons olive oil
3 oz belly pork, or unsmoked bacon
2 tomatoes
1 carrot
1 clove garlic
few shreds thinly pared orange rind
bouquet garni
salt and pepper
scant ¼ pint red wine

Potato Croquettes

Peel the potatoes and cook in boiling salted water until tender, about 15 minutes. Drain and dry off in the pan over a moderate heat. Rub the potatoes though a sieve, or potato ricer, and return to the pan. Separate the egg, reserving the white on a plate, and beat the yolk, the butter and hot milk into the potatoes. Season with salt and pepper.

Lightly whisk the egg white with a fork, and divide the potato mixture into balls roughly the size of a large walnut. With floured hands, shape the balls into rolls, brush with the egg white and roll in the breadcrumbs. At this stage the croquettes may be set aside in the refrigerator, or even stored in a freezer in a plastic bag, if made in advance. If frozen, remember to thaw out for 2 or 3 hours. To serve, fry in hot deep fat until golden brown.

¾ lb potatoes
1 egg
small nut of butter
2 tablespoons hot milk
salt and pepper
toasted breadcrumbs

Small Brussels Sprouts and Chestnuts

Cut a slit in the flat side of about a dozen chestnuts and place in a saucepan of boiling water. Simmer for 10 minutes. Drain and peel away the outer and inner skins. Cook the peeled chestnuts in a pan of boiling salted water for 20 minutes, drain and set aside.

When you cook the Brussels sprouts, drop the chestnuts into the pan of boiling water with the sprouts. Cook for 7

1 doz chestnuts
1 lb Brussels sprouts
salt
melted butter

minutes, when the sprouts will be tender, but crisp, and the chestnuts heated through. Drain well, and toss in melted butter.

Bavarian Cream with Praline

Put the almonds and sugar into a small pan. Set over a low heat until the sugar has melted. As the mixture starts to turn golden brown, stir with a metal spoon until the brown is deeper and the almonds glazed. Turn at once into an oiled tin, and leave until set hard.

Heat the milk in a small saucepan until nearly boiling. Put the water in a small pan and sprinkle on the gelatine, soak for 5 minutes.

Put the egg yolks into a basin, add the sugar, and beat together until thick and light. Add the hot milk slowly to the egg mixture, stirring all the time, then return to the saucepan, add the soaked gelatine and stir over a low heat for a minute or two until the gelatine has dissolved. Strain into a bowl and set aside.

When the mixture has cooled and started to thicken, fold in the lightly whipped cream.

Turn the praline on to a clean board, and crush to a coarse powder with a rolling pin. Fold 2 tablespoons of praline into the mixture. Pour at once into a small soufflé dish and leave to set. Decorate with a piped border of whipped cream before serving.

For the Praline
2 oz unblanched almonds
2 oz sugar

For the cream
6 fl oz milk
2 tablespoons water
¼ oz powdered gelatine
2 egg yolks
1 oz sugar
¼ pint heavy (double) cream

Acknowledgments

The authors and publishers wish to thank the institutions and persons mentioned below for permission to reproduce works in their possession, and to record their gratitude to the staffs of the Departments of Prints and Drawings of the British Library and of the British Museum, Department of Oriental Antiquities, as well as to those of the Victoria and Albert Museum, London, and of the Bibliothèque de l'Arsenal, Paris, for their patience and expert assistance.

The illustrations

Page 126/127   *Le Matin* by Nicolas Lancret (1690–1743) in the National Gallery, London (5867)

128   *L'Amant Ecouté* by L. M. Bonnet after J. B. Huet, 1745–84, in the British Museum, London

129   Miniature from folio 139*r* of Cod. Guelf 8.7. Aug. 4° in Herzog August Bibliothek, Wolfenbüttel

130   Miniature from *Faites et Paroles Mémorables de Valère Maxime,* Bibliothèque Nationale, Paris

131   Detail from a painting by Pieter Isacsin in Statens Museum fur Kunst, Copenhagen

132   Paul Gavarni: *Un Cabinet chez Petron* (1833)

133/134   A painting by G. Schalken, 1643–1706, in The National Gallery, London (999)

135   Two lovers at table by Hendrik Sorgh, 1610–1670, in The National Gallery, London (1056)

136   A painting by Adriaen van Ostade, 1610–1685, in The National Gallery, London (2542)

169   A Persian miniature of about 1590 in the Isfahan style now in the Victoria and Albert Museum, London (692–1876–16)

170   A 19th-century Chinese painting in the British Museum, London (1877–7–14–1082)

Page 171   A Chinese painting of A.D. 1697 in the British Museum, London (Ch. Ptg. Add. 219, f.13)

172   A painting by Koriusai in a Japanese album in the British Museum, London (Box XVIII 1931–5–13–023)

173   A painting by Harunobu in a Japanese album in the British Museum, London (Box XIV 1937–7–10–042)

174   Prosita pateka Nayika (Punch, *circa* 1790) in the Victoria and Albert Museum, London (I.S. 103–1951)

175   An illustration for the Vibhasa Ragina, Tonk. 18th century, now in the Victoria and Albert Museum, London (I.M. 45–1911)

176/177   Édouard Manet: *Chex le Père Lathuille.* Musée de Cambrai

178   Toulouse-Lautrec: *Le Lit.* Musée National du Louvre, Paris

179   Auguste Renoir: *The Café.* Now in the collection of Kröller-Müller Stichting at Otterloo (Cat. 577)

180/181   Two lithographs that Toulouse-Lautrec did for menu cards

182/183   Édouard Manet: *Déjeuner sur l'Herbe* Musée National du Louvre, Paris

184   *Bank Holiday* by W. Strang. The Cupid Press, Ipswich

Index